BIG IDEAS
MATH®
Modeling Real Life

Grade 6

Student Journal

- Review & Refresh
- Exploration Journal
- Practice Worksheets
- Notetaking with Vocabulary
- Self-Assessments
- Exploration Manipulatives

BIG IDEAS
LEARNING®

Erie, Pennsylvania

About the Student Journal

Review & Refresh

The Review & Refresh provides students the opportunity to practice prior skills necessary to move forward.

Exploration Journal

The Exploration pages correspond to the Exploration in the Pupil Edition. Here students have room to show their work and record their answers.

Practice Worksheets

Each section of the Pupil Edition has an additional practice on the key concepts taught in the lesson.

Notetaking with Vocabulary

The student-friendly notetaking component is designed to be a reference for key vocabulary from the lesson. There is room for students to add definition to their words and take notes about key ideas.

Self-Assessment

For every lesson, students can rate their understanding of the learning target and success criteria.

Exploration Manipulatives

Manipulatives needed for the explorations are included in the back of the Student Journal.

Printed in the United States

ISBN 13: 978-1-64208-081-0

3456789-22 21 20 19

Contents

Contents

Contents

Contents

Contents

Contents

Contents

Contents

10.5   Box-and-Whisker Plots

Name_____ Date _____

Chapter 1 Review & Refresh

Determine whether the number is prime or composite.

1. 4

2. 7

3. 13

4. 22

5. 19

6. 27

7. 30

8. 37

9. 41

10. 45

11. You have 33 marbles. Besides 1 group of 33 marbles, is it possible to divide the marbles into groups with the same number of marbles with no marbles left over?

12. You have 43 pencils. Besides 1 group of 43 pencils, is it possible to divide the pencils into groups with the same number of pencils with no pencils left over?

Name _____ Date _____

Add or subtract.

13. $1\frac{1}{5} + 1\frac{3}{5}$

14. $2\frac{3}{7} + 3\frac{2}{7}$

15. $4\frac{5}{9} + 6\frac{2}{9}$

16. $3\frac{6}{11} + 5\frac{4}{11}$

17. $4\frac{3}{4} - 2\frac{1}{4}$

18. $5\frac{3}{8} - 3\frac{7}{8}$

19. $2\frac{3}{10} - 1\frac{7}{10}$

20. $6\frac{5}{12} - 2\frac{11}{12}$

21. You are baking cookies. You have $7\frac{1}{4}$ cups of flour. You use $2\frac{3}{4}$ cups of flour. How much flour do you have left?

Name_____ Date _____

Powers and Exponents
For use with Exploration 1.1

Learning Target: Write and evaluate expressions involving exponents.

Success Criteria:
- I can write products of repeated factors as powers.
- I can evaluate powers.

1 EXPLORATION: Writing Expressions Using Exponents

Work with a partner. Complete the table.

Repeated Factors	Using an Exponent	Value
a. 10×10		
b. 4×4		
c. 6×6		
d. $10 \times 10 \times 10$		
e. $100 \times 100 \times 100$		
f. $3 \times 3 \times 3 \times 3$		
g. $4 \times 4 \times 4 \times 4 \times 4$		
h. $2 \times 2 \times 2 \times 2 \times 2 \times 2$		

i. In your own words, describe what the two numbers in the expression 3^5 mean.

1.1 **Powers and Exponents** (continued)

2 EXPLORATION: Using a Calculator to Find a Pattern

Work with a partner. Use a calculator to find each value. Write one digit of the value in each box. Describe the pattern in the digits of the values.

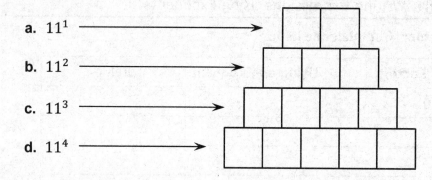

a. 11^1

b. 11^2

c. 11^3

d. 11^4

Name_____ Date _____

1.1 Notetaking with Vocabulary

Vocabulary:

Notes:

1.1 Self-Assessment

Use the scale below to rate your understanding of the learning target and the success criteria.

1	2	3	4
I do not understand.	I can do it with help.	I can do it on my own.	I can teach someone else.

	Rating	Date
1.1 Powers and Exponents		
Learning Target: Write and evaluate expressions involving exponents.	1 2 3 4	
I can write products of repeated factors as powers.	1 2 3 4	
I can evaluate powers.	1 2 3 4	

Name_____ Date _____

1.1 Practice

1. Describe and correct the error in writing the value of the product.

$$\times \quad 7^5 = 7 \times 5 = 35$$

Write the product as a power.

2. $81 \cdot 81 \cdot 81 \cdot 81$ 3. $500 \times 500 \times 500$ 4. $p \cdot p \cdot p \cdot p \cdot p \cdot p$

Find the value of the power.

5. 2^3 6. 10^6 7. 3^5

8. There are 3 water slides in the park, arranged from shortest to tallest. The shortest slide is 3 feet tall. The height of each water slide is three times the height of the previous water slide. Write a power to represent the height of the tallest water slide. Then find the height.

9. A square closet measures 6 feet on each side. What is the area of the closet in square yards?

10. The number 75 falls between what two perfect squares?

11. The number 300 falls between what two perfect squares?

12. Write the perfect squares that are greater than 150 and less than 250.

13. Write three powers that have values greater than 500 and less than 550.

14. A homeowner would like to modify the existing patio to create a square patio, either by adding new tiles or moving existing tiles. Each tile is one foot square. The current patio is shown.

    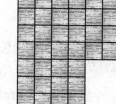

    a. Find the area of the existing patio by dividing the patio in to two or more pieces.

    b. How could the homeowner rearrange the existing tiles to create a square patio without adding new tiles?

    c. How many tiles must the homeowner purchase to create a patio that has 7 feet on each side? Can this be done without moving any of the existing tiles?

    d. To create a patio that is 25 square feet, the homeowner must move some tiles and remove others. How many tiles must be moved and how many tiles must be removed?

1.2 Order of Operations
For use with Exploration 1.2

Learning Target: Write and evaluate numerical expressions using the order of operations.

Success Criteria:
- I can explain why there is a need for a standard order of operations.
- I can evaluate numerical expressions involving several operations, exponents, and grouping symbols.
- I can write numerical expressions involving exponents to represent a real-life problem.

1 EXPLORATION: Comparing Different Orders

Work with a partner. Find the value of each expression by using different orders of operations. Are your answers the same?

a. Add, then multiply.   Multiply, then add.

$3 + 2 \times 2$ $3 + 2 \times 2$

b. Subtract, then multiply.   Multiply, then subtract.

$18 - 3 \cdot 3$ $18 - 3 \cdot 3$

c. Multiply, then subtract.   Subtract, then multiply.

$8 \times 8 - 2$ $8 \times 8 - 2$

d. Multiply, then add.   Add, then multiply.

$6 \cdot 6 + 2$ $6 \cdot 6 + 2$

1.2 **Order of Operations** (continued)

2 **EXPLORATION:** Determining Order of Operations

Work with a partner.

a. Scientific calculators use a standard order of operations when evaluating expressions. Why is a standard order of operations needed?

b. Use a scientific calculator to evaluate each expression in Exploration 1. Enter each expression exactly as written. For each expression, which order of operations is correct?

c. What order of operations should be used to evaluate $3 + 2^2$, $18 - 3^2$, $8^2 - 2$, and $6^2 + 2$?

d. Do $18 \div 3 \cdot 3$ and $18 \div 3^2$ have the same value? Justify your answer.

e. How does evaluating powers fit into the order of operations?

1.2 Notetaking with Vocabulary

Vocabulary:

Notes:

1.2 Self-Assessment

Use the scale below to rate your understanding of the learning target and the success criteria.

1	2	3	4
I do not understand.	I can do it with help.	I can do it on my own.	I can teach someone else.

	Rating	Date
1.2 Order of Operations		
Learning Target: Write and evaluate numerical expressions using the order of operations.	1 2 3 4	
I can explain why there is a need for a standard order of operations.	1 2 3 4	
I can evaluate numerical expressions involving several operations, exponents, and grouping symbols.	1 2 3 4	
I can write numerical expressions involving exponents to represent a real-life problem.	1 2 3 4	

1.2 Practice

Evaluate each expression. Are the two expressions equal? Explain your answer.

1. a. $(100 \div 5) \times 4$ b. $100 \div 5 \times 4$

2. a. $\dfrac{12}{2+4}$ b. $\dfrac{12}{2} + 4$

3. a. $\dfrac{18}{6-3}$ b. $18 \div (6-3)$

4. There are 34 people in a restaurant. Four groups of 3 people leave, and then 5 groups of 2 people arrive. Evaluate the expression $34 - 4 \cdot 3 + 5 \cdot 2$ to determine how many people are in the restaurant.

Evaluate the expression.

5. $\dfrac{11^2 - 5 + 4(7)}{(4)(3)}$ 6. $\dfrac{54 \div 6 + 31}{4^2 + 4}$

7. A group of 8 students purchase 4 pizzas at $5 each, 2 orders of breadsticks at $2 each, and 8 drinks at $1.50 each. How much does each student owe before tax? Explain how you solved the problem.

8. Five sandwich rings are each cut into 4 pieces. You then cut each of the pieces into 3 servings. How many servings do you have?

9. Use all four operations and at least one exponent to write an expression that has a value of 10.

10. Insert $+$, $-$, $\times$, or $\div$ symbols to make each statement true.

    a. $17 \underline{} 2 \underline{} 3 \underline{} 8 = 3$

    b. $33 \underline{} 3 \underline{} 2 \underline{} 5 = 1$

    c. $6^2 \underline{} 6 \underline{} 2 \underline{} 3 = 45$

    d. $8^2 \underline{} 4 \underline{} 2 \underline{} 2 = 4$

1.3 **Prime Factorization**
For use with Exploration 1.3

Learning Target: Write a number as a product of prime factors and represent the product using exponents.

Success Criteria:
- I can find factor pairs of a number.
- I can explain the meanings of prime and composite numbers
- I can create a factor tree to find the prime factors of a number.
- I can write the prime factorization of a number.

1 **EXPLORATION:** Rewriting Numbers as Products of Factors

Work with a partner. Two students use *factor trees* **to write 108 as a product of factors, as shown below.**

Student A	**Student B**

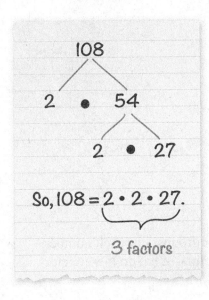
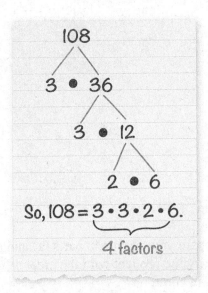

a. Without using 1 as a factor, can you write 108 as a product with more factors than each student used? Justify your answer.

1.3 **Prime Factorization** (continued)

b. Use factor trees to write 80, 162, and 300 as products of as many factors as possible. Do not use 1 as a factor.

c. Compare your results in parts (a) and (b) with other groups. For each number, identify the product with the greatest number of factors. What do these factors have in common?

Notetaking with Vocabulary

Vocabulary:

Notes:

1.3 Self-Assessment

Use the scale below to rate your understanding of the learning target and the success criteria.

1	2	3	4
I do not understand.	I can do it with help.	I can do it on my own.	I can teach someone else.

	Rating	Date
1.3 Prime Factorization		
Learning Target: Write a number as a product of prime factors and represent the product using exponents.	1 2 3 4	
I can find factor pairs of a number.	1 2 3 4	
I can explain the meanings of prime and composite numbers.	1 2 3 4	
I can create a factor tree to find the prime factors of a number.	1 2 3 4	
I can write the prime factorization of a number.	1 2 3 4	

1.3 Practice

1. Describe and correct the error in writing the factor pairs of 30.

> ✗ 30 = 2 · 15
> 30 = 3 · 10
> 30 = 5 · 6

Find the greatest perfect square that is a factor of the number.

2. 693

3. 720

4. 51,425

5. The prime factorization of a number is the product of the first 5 prime numbers. Find the number.

6. A coach divides 24 athletes into equal groups for a practice drill. Each group should have at least 3 athletes but no more than 5 athletes. What are the possible group sizes?

7. One table at a bake sale has 150 mini cupcakes. Another table has 180 mini cookies. Which table allows for more square arrangements when all the mini cupcakes and mini cookies are displayed? Explain.

8. A friend is building a dog pen with an area of 150 square feet. Each side must be at least 5 feet long, using only whole number dimensions.

    a. List all possible dimensions of the dog pen.

    b. Which dimension gives you the maximum amount of fence required to build the dog pen, and how much fence does it require?

    c. What dimensions would provide the longest running path for the dog?

9. Consider the rectangular prism shown. Using only whole number dimensions, how many different prisms are possible? Explain.

Rectangular Prism

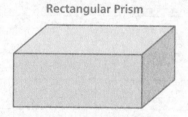

Volume = 54 cubic inches

1.4 Greatest Common Factor
For use with Exploration 1.4

Learning Target: Find the greatest common factor of two numbers.

Success Criteria:
- I can explain the meaning of factors of a number.
- I can use lists of factors to identify the greatest common factor of numbers.
- I can use prime factors to identify the greatest common factor of numbers.

A **Venn diagram** uses circles to describe relationships between two or more sets. The Venn diagram shows the factors of 12 and 15. Numbers that are factors of both 12 and 15 are represented by the overlap of the two circles.

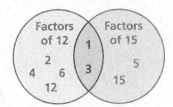

---

1 **EXPLORATION: Identifying Common Factors**

Work with a partner. In parts (a)-(d), create a Venn diagram that represents the factors of each number and identify any *common factors*.

a. 36 and 48

b. 16 and 56

c. 30 and 75

d. 54 and 90

e. Look at the Venn diagrams in parts (a)-(d). Explain how to identify the *greatest common factor* of each pair of numbers. Then circle it in each diagram.

Name_____ Date _____

2 **EXPLORATION:** Using Prime Factors

Work with a partner.

    a. Each Venn diagram represents the prime factorizations of two numbers.
    Identify each pair of numbers. Explain your reasoning.

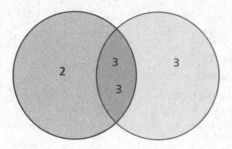 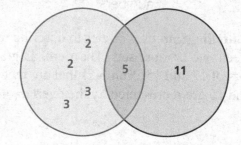

    b. Create a Venn diagram that represents the prime factorizations of 36 and 48.

    c. Repeat part (b) for the remaining number pairs in Exploration 1.

    d. Make a conjecture about the relationship between the greatest common
    factors you found in Exploration 1 and the numbers in the overlaps of the
    Venn diagrams you just created.

1.4 Notetaking with Vocabulary

Vocabulary:

Notes:

1.4 Self-Assessment

Use the scale below to rate your understanding of the learning target and the success criteria.

1	2	3	4
I do not understand.	I can do it with help.	I can do it on my own.	I can teach someone else.

	Rating	Date
1.4 Greatest Common Factor		
Learning Target: Find the greatest common factor of two numbers.	1 2 3 4	
I can explain the meaning of factors of a number.	1 2 3 4	
I can use lists of factors to identify the greatest common factor of numbers.	1 2 3 4	
I can use prime factors to identify the greatest common factor of numbers.	1 2 3 4	

Name_____ Date _____

1.4 Practice

1. Describe and correct the error in finding the GCF of 10 and 18.

   $$10 = 2 \cdot 5$$
   $$18 = 2 \cdot 3^2$$
   The GCF is 90.

2. You are making flower arrangements for a party. There are 18 lilies and 27 carnations. Each arrangement must be identical. What is the greatest number of arrangements you can make using every lily and every carnation?

3. You are creating a set of three numbers that have a GCF of 9. You have 27 and 54 for two of the numbers.

   a. What is the GCF of 27 and 54?

   b. Find two numbers that you could add to the set of 27 and 54 such that the GCF is now 9.

Tell whether the statement is *always*, *sometimes*, or *never* true. Explain your reasoning.

4. The GCF of two even numbers is even.

5. The GCF of two odd numbers is odd.

6. When one number is even and the other number is odd, the GCF of the numbers is even.

7. When one number is the square of the other number, the GCF of the numbers is the least of the numbers.

8. Consider the numbers 308, 616, and 660.

   a. Find the prime factorization of each number.

   b. Find the GCF of each pair of numbers.

   c. Which pair of numbers has a different GCF than the other two pairs?

   d. Find the GCF of all three numbers.

1.5 Least Common Multiple
For use with Exploration 1.5

Learning Target: Find the least common multiple of two numbers.

Success Criteria:
- I can explain the meaning of multiples of a number.
- I can use lists of multiples to identify the least common multiple of numbers.
- I can use prime factors to identify the least common multiple of numbers.

1 EXPLORATION: Identifying Common Multiples

Work with a partner. In parts (a)-(d), create a Venn diagram that represents the first several multiples of each number and identify any *common multiples*.

a. 8 and 12

b. 4 and 14

c. 10 and 15

d. 20 and 35

e. Look at the Venn diagrams in parts (a)-(d). Explain how to identify the *least common multiple* of each pair of numbers. Then circle it in each diagram.

1.5 **Least Common Multiple** (continued)

2 **EXPLORATION:** Using Prime Factors

Work with a partner.

a. Create a Venn diagram that represents the prime factorizations of 8 and 12.

b. Repeat part (a) for the remaining number pairs in Exploration 1.

c. Make a conjecture about the relationship between the least common multiples you found in Exploration 1 and the numbers in the Venn diagrams you just created.

d. The Venn diagram shows the prime factors of two numbers. Use the diagram to complete the following tasks.

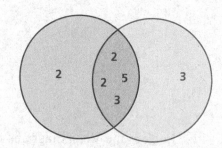

  • Identify the two numbers.

  • Find the greatest common factor.

  • Find the least common multiple.

Notetaking with Vocabulary

Vocabulary:

Notes:

1.5 Self-Assessment

Use the scale below to rate your understanding of the learning target and the success criteria.

1	2	3	4
I do not understand.	I can do it with help.	I can do it on my own.	I can teach someone else.

	Rating	Date
1.5 Least Common Multiple		
Learning Target: Find the least common multiple of two numbers.	1 2 3 4	
I can explain the meaning of multiples of a number.	1 2 3 4	
I can use lists of multiples to identify the least common multiple of numbers.	1 2 3 4	
I can use prime factors to identify the least common multiple of numbers.	1 2 3 4	

1.5 Practice

1. You run one lap around a mile track every 8 minutes. Your friend runs around the same track every 10 minutes. You both start at the starting line at the same time.

   a. How far have each of you run when you first meet again at the starting line?

   b. How far have each of you run the next time you meet at the starting line?

2. Plastic plates come in packs of 8, plastic utensils come in packs of 12, and plastic cups come in packs of 20. What are the least numbers of packs you should buy in order to have the same number of plates, utensils, and cups?

Tell whether the statement is *always*, *sometimes*, or *never* true.

3. The GCF of two different numbers is greater than the LCM of the numbers.

4. The LCM of a prime number and a composite number is a multiple of the prime number.

5. A theater gives away one free ticket to every 10th customer and two free tickets to every 25th customer. The manager wants to give away four free tickets when the customer is both a 10th and a 25th customer.

   a. Who is the first customer that will receive four free tickets?

   b. If 120 customers have bought tickets today, how many free tickets has the manager given away?

6. At Central Station, you notice that three metro lines just arrived at the same time. The table shows their arrival schedule. How long must you wait until all three lines arrive at Central Station at the same time again?

Metro Line	Arrival Time
A	every 8 minutes
B	every 12 minutes
C	every 15 minutes

Name_____ Date _____

Chapter Self-Assessment

Use the scale below to rate your understanding of the learning target and the success criteria.

1	2	3	4
I do not understand.	I can do it with help.	I can do it on my own.	I can teach someone else.

	Rating	Date
1.1 Powers and Exponents		
Learning Target: Write and evaluate expressions involving exponents.	1 2 3 4	
I can write products of repeated factors as powers.	1 2 3 4	
I can evaluate powers.	1 2 3 4	
1.2 Order of Operations		
Learning Target: Write and evaluate numerical expressions using the order of operations.	1 2 3 4	
I can explain why there is a need for a standard order of operations.	1 2 3 4	
I can evaluate numerical expressions involving several operations, exponents, and grouping symbols.	1 2 3 4	
I can write numerical expressions involving exponents to represent a real-life problem.	1 2 3 4	
1.3 Prime Factorization		
Learning Target: Write a number as a product of prime factors and represent the product using exponents.	1 2 3 4	
I can find factor pairs of a number.	1 2 3 4	
I can explain the meanings of prime and composite numbers.	1 2 3 4	
I can create a factor tree to find the prime factors of a number.	1 2 3 4	
I can write the prime factorization of a number.	1 2 3 4	

Name _____ Date _____

Chapter 1 Chapter Self-Assessment (continued)

	Rating	Date
1.4 Greatest Common Factor		
Learning Target: Find the greatest common factor of two numbers.	1 2 3 4	
I can explain the meaning of factors of a number.	1 2 3 4	
I can use lists of factors to identify the greatest common factor of numbers.	1 2 3 4	
I can use prime factors to identify the greatest common factor of numbers.	1 2 3 4	
1.5 Least Common Multiple		
Learning Target: Find the least common multiple of two numbers.	1 2 3 4	
I can explain the meaning of multiples of a number.	1 2 3 4	
I can use lists of multiples to identify the least common multiple of numbers.	1 2 3 4	
I can use prime factors to identify the least common multiple of numbers.	1 2 3 4	

Chapter 2 **Review & Refresh**

Estimate the product or quotient.

1. 91×17

2. 57×29

3. $83 \div 18$

4. $204 \div 9$

5. $152 \div 31$

6. 13×78

7. 32×51

8. $651 \div 49$

9. There are 546 people attending a charity event. You are baking cookies to give away. Each batch makes 48 cookies. Estimate the number of batches you need to make so that each person gets one cookie.

Review & Refresh (continued)

Find the product or quotient.

10. 351×15

11. 187×27

12. $333 \div 9$

13. $474 \div 3$

14. A bleacher row can seat 14 people. The bleachers are filled to capacity with 1330 people at a soccer game. How many rows of bleachers does the soccer field have?

Name_____ Date _____

 Multiplying Fractions
For use with Exploration 2.1

Learning Target: Find products involving fractions and mixed numbers.

Success Criteria:
- I can draw a model to explain fraction multiplication.
- I can multiply fractions.
- I can find products involving mixed numbers.
- I can interpret products involving fractions and mixed numbers to solve real-life problems.

1 EXPLORATION: Using Models to Solve a Problem

Work with a partner. A bottle of water is $\frac{1}{2}$ full. You drink $\frac{2}{3}$ of the water.
Use one of the models to find the portion of the bottle of water that you drink.
Explain your steps.

- number line

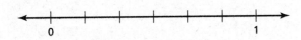

- area model

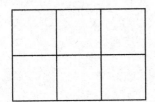

- tape diagram

2.1 **Multiplying Fractions** (continued)

---

2 **EXPLORATION:** Solving a Problem Involving Fractions

Work with a partner. A park has a playground that is $\frac{3}{4}$ of its width and $\frac{4}{5}$ of its length.

  a. Use a model to find the portion of the park that is covered by the playground. Explain your steps.

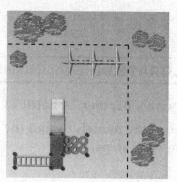

  b. How can you find the solution of part (a) without using a model?

Name_____ Date_____

 2.1 **Notetaking with Vocabulary**

Vocabulary:

Notes:

 **2.1** **Self-Assessment**

Use the scale below to rate your understanding of the learning target and the success criteria.

1	2	3	4
I do not understand.	I can do it with help.	I can do it on my own.	I can teach someone else.

	Rating	Date
2.1 Multiplying Fractions		
Learning Target: Find products involving fractions and mixed numbers.	1 2 3 4	
I can draw a model to explain fraction multiplication.	1 2 3 4	
I can multiply fractions.	1 2 3 4	
I can find products involving mixed numbers.	1 2 3 4	
I can interpret products involving fractions and mixed numbers to solve real-life problems.	1 2 3 4	

2.1 Practice

1. Describe and correct the error in finding the product.

   $$\cancel{}\quad \frac{5}{6} \times \frac{5}{6} = \frac{5 \times 5}{6} = \frac{25}{6} = 4\frac{1}{6}$$

2. One-half of your CDs are scratched. Of those, one-fifth will not play properly. You have 40 CDs. How many of them will not play properly?

3. You are making a poster with a partial border (the shaded region).

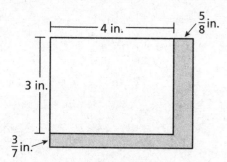

   a. Find the area of the partial border. Explain how you found the area.

   b. Using mixed numbers, write the expression to find the entire area (poster and partial border).

   c. Multiply the expression in part (b). Write the answer in simplest form.

   d. Subtract the answer in part (a) from the answer in part (c). Explain what this represents.

4. Find a fraction that, when multiplied by $\frac{1}{3}$, is greater than $\frac{1}{4}$ and less than $\frac{1}{2}$.

5. You ask 120 people about their computer preference. The results show that $\frac{11}{12}$ of the people own a laptop computer. Of the people who own a laptop computer, $\frac{1}{10}$ of them also own a desktop computer.

   a. What portion of the people own a laptop computer and a desktop computer?

   b. How many people own a laptop computer but not a desktop computer? Explain.

Dividing Fractions
For use with Exploration 2.2

Learning Target: Compute quotients of fractions and solve problems involving division by fractions.

Success Criteria:
- I can draw a model to explain division of fractions.
- I can find reciprocals of numbers.
- I can divide fractions by fractions.
- I can divide fractions and whole numbers.

1 EXPLORATION: Dividing by Fractions

Work with a partner. Answer each question using a model.

a. How many two-thirds are in four?

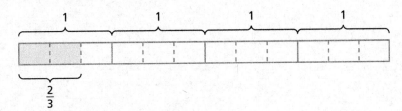

b. How many three-fourths are in three?

c. How many two-fifths are in four-fifths?

d. How many two-thirds are in three?

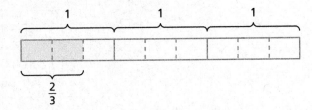

e. How many one-thirds are in five-sixths?

2.2 **Dividing Fractions** (continued)

2 **EXPLORATION:** Finding a Pattern

Work with a partner. The table shows the division expressions from Exploration 1. Complete each multiplication expression so that it has the same value as the division expression above it. What can you conclude about dividing by fractions?

Division Expression	$4 \div \dfrac{2}{3}$	$3 \div \dfrac{3}{4}$	$\dfrac{4}{5} \div \dfrac{2}{5}$	$3 \div \dfrac{2}{3}$	$\dfrac{5}{6} \div \dfrac{1}{3}$
Multiplication Expression	$4 \times ?$	$3 \times ?$	$\dfrac{4}{5} \times ?$	$3 \times ?$	$\dfrac{5}{6} \times ?$

Notetaking with Vocabulary

Vocabulary:

Notes:

 Self-Assessment

Use the scale below to rate your understanding of the learning target and the success criteria.

1	2	3	4
I do not understand.	I can do it with help.	I can do it on my own.	I can teach someone else.

	Rating	Date
2.2 Dividing Fractions		
Learning Target: Compute quotients of fractions and solve problems involving division by fractions.	1 2 3 4	
I can draw a model to explain division of fractions.	1 2 3 4	
I can find reciprocals of numbers.	1 2 3 4	
I can divide fractions by fractions.	1 2 3 4	
I can divide fractions and whole numbers.	1 2 3 4	

Name _____ Date _____

2.2 Practice

1. Describe and correct the error in finding the quotient.

$$\cancel{}\quad \frac{3}{5} \div \frac{9}{10} = \frac{5}{3} \cdot \frac{10}{9} = \frac{50}{27} = 1\frac{23}{27}$$

2. You have $\frac{5}{8}$ of a pepperoni pizza. You divide the remaining pizza into 3 equal slices. What portion of the original pizza is each slice?

Complete the statement.

3. $\frac{1}{6} \times$ ___ $= 1$

4. $8 \div$ ___ $= 40$

5. $\frac{11}{3} \div$ ___ $= 11$

Without finding the quotient, complete the statement using <, >, or =. Explain your reasoning.

6. $4 \div \frac{6}{7}$ ___ 4

7. $1 \div \frac{2}{3}$ ___ 1

8. $\frac{4}{5} \div \frac{9}{10}$ ___ $\frac{4}{5}$

9. When is the reciprocal of a fraction the same as the fraction? Explain.

10. How many times larger is a 10-pound dog than a hamster weighing $\frac{5}{8}$ pounds?

11. A container of coffee is $\frac{1}{6}$ full. The container contains $\frac{2}{3}$ of a pound of coffee.

   a. Write a division expression that represents the capacity of the container.

   b. Write a related multiplication expression that represents the capacity of the container.

   c. Find the capacity of the container.

12. A digital camera memory card is $\frac{1}{4}$ full. The card is $\frac{2}{3}$ full when 375 more pictures have been taken.

   a. How many pictures can the memory card hold?

   b. How many pictures were originally on the memory card?

   c. How many pictures are on the memory card when it is $\frac{5}{6}$ full?

2.3 Dividing Mixed Numbers
For use with Exploration 2.3

Learning Target: Compute quotients with mixed numbers and solve problems involving division with mixed numbers.

Success Criteria:
- I can draw a model to explain division of mixed numbers.
- I can write a mixed number as an improper fraction.
- I can divide with mixed numbers.
- I can evaluate expressions involving mixed numbers using the order of operations.

1 EXPLORATION: Dividing Mixed Numbers

Work with a partner. Write a real-life problem that represents each division expression described. Then solve each problem using a model. Check your answers.

  a. How many three-fourths are in four and one-half?

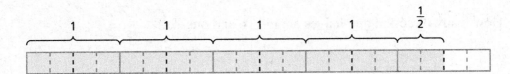

  b. How many three-eighths are in two and one-fourth?

  c. How many one and one-halves are in six?

2.3 **Dividing Mixed Numbers** (continued)

   d. How many seven-sixths are in three and one-third?

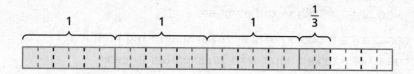

   e. How many one and one-fifths are in five?

   f. How many three and one-halves are in two and one-half?

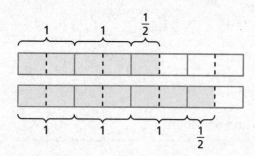

   g. How many four and one-halves are in one and one-half?

Name_____ Date _____

2.3 Notetaking with Vocabulary

Vocabulary:

Notes:

2.3 Self-Assessment

Use the scale below to rate your understanding of the learning target and the success criteria.

		Rating	Date
2.3 Dividing Mixed Numbers			
Learning Target: Compute quotients with mixed numbers and solve problems involving division with mixed numbers.		1 2 3 4	
I can draw a model to explain division of mixed numbers.		1 2 3 4	
I can write a mixed number as an improper fraction.		1 2 3 4	
I can divide with mixed numbers.		1 2 3 4	
I can evaluate expressions involving mixed numbers using the order of operations.		1 2 3 4	

2.3 Practice

1. Describe and correct the error in finding the quotient.

$$\times \quad 8\frac{1}{3} \div 15 = \frac{25}{3} \div 15 = 15 \times \frac{3}{25} = \frac{45}{25} = \frac{9}{5} = 1\frac{4}{5}$$

2. How many times longer is a $20\frac{2}{5}$-meter garden path than a $6\frac{4}{5}$-meter garden path?

3. You have 187 yards of ribbon to attach to balloons. Each balloon will have the same length of ribbon. You want to use all of the ribbon. Should each ribbon be $7\frac{1}{2}$, $8\frac{1}{2}$, or $9\frac{1}{2}$ feet long? Explain.

4. How many $3\frac{3}{4}$-inch wires can be cut from a spool of wire that is 100 inches long? Will there be any wire left over? If so, how much?

5. A bag of fertilizer that weighs $18\frac{3}{4}$ pounds can cover 5000 square feet.

   a. How many pounds of fertilizer will be needed to cover 27,000 square feet?

   b. How many bags of fertilizer are needed? Explain how you found your answer.

6. A package contains 56 cups of oatmeal. A batch of cookies requires $2\frac{3}{4}$ cups of oatmeal. Is there enough oatmeal to make 21 batches of cookies? Explain.

7. You have $14\frac{1}{2}$ cups of granola and 10 cups of peanuts to make trail mix. One batch of trail mix consists of $2\frac{3}{4}$ cups of granola and $1\frac{1}{3}$ cups of peanuts. What is the greatest number of full batches of trail mix you can make? Explain how you found your answer.

8. At a track and field meet, the longest discus throw by a 7th grader is 65 feet 4 inches. The longest discus throw by a 6th grader is 54 feet 7 inches. How many times greater is the longest discus throw by the 7th grader than by the 6th grader?

Adding and Subtracting Decimals
For use with Exploration 2.4

Learning Target: Add and subtract decimals and solve problems involving addition and subtraction of decimals.

Success Criteria:
- I can explain why it is necessary to line up the decimal points when adding and subtracting decimals.
- I can add decimals.
- I can subtract decimals.
- I can evaluate expressions involving addition and subtraction of decimals.

 EXPLORATION: Using Number Lines

Work with a partner. Use each number line to find $A + B$ and $B - A$. Explain how you know you are correct.

a.

b.
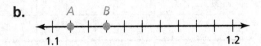

c.
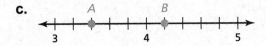

d.

Name_____ Date _____

2.4 **Adding and Subtracting Decimals** (continued)

2 **EXPLORATION:** Extending the Place Value Chart

Work with a partner. Explain how you can use the place value chart below to add and subtract decimals beyond hundredths. Then find each sum or difference.

Place Value Chart

millions	hundred thousands	ten thousands	thousands	hundreds	tens	ones	and	tenths	hundredths		
							•				
							•				
							•				

a. $16.05 + 2.945$

b. $7.421 + 8.058$

c. $38.72 - 8.618$

d. $64.968 - 51.167$

e. $225.1 + 85.0465$

f. $1107.20592 - 102.3056$

Student Journal

Copyright © Big Ideas Learning, LLC
All rights reserved.

2.4 Notetaking with Vocabulary

Vocabulary:

Notes:

2.4 Self-Assessment

Use the scale below to rate your understanding of the learning target and the success criteria.

1	**2**	**3**	**4**
I do not understand.	I can do it with help.	I can do it on my own.	I can teach someone else.

	Rating	Date
2.4 Adding and Subtracting Decimals		
Learning Target: Add and subtract decimals and solve problems involving addition and subtraction of decimals.	1 2 3 4	
I can explain why it is necessary to line up the decimal points when adding and subtracting decimals.	1 2 3 4	
I can add decimals.	1 2 3 4	
I can subtract decimals.	1 2 3 4	
I can evaluate expressions involving addition and subtraction of decimals.	1 2 3 4	

2.4 Practice

1. The large bottle of nasal spray is 9.46 centimeters tall. The small bottle is 5.29 centimeters tall. How much shorter is the small bottle than the large bottle?

2. A child must weigh no more than 34.5 pounds to ride in a particular car seat.

   a. A child weighs 36.269 pounds. By how many pounds does the child exceed the weight limit?

   b. A child weighs 31.833 pounds. How many pounds can the child gain before needing a new car seat?

3. The table shows the dimensions, in inches, of two picture frames that are in the shape of right triangles.

	Leg 1	Leg 2	Hypotenuse
Frame A	3	6.2	6.888
Frame B	4.2	5.1	6.607

   a. How much larger is the hypotenuse of Frame A than Frame B?

   b. What is the perimeter of Frame A?

   c. What is the perimeter of Frame B?

   d. What is the sum of the two perimeters?

   e. Find the sum of the two legs of each picture frame. Which frame has the larger sum of two legs?

4. At Station M, the price of gas is $3.319 per gallon and the price of diesel is $4.429 per gallon.

   a. You buy 2 gallons of gas and your friend buys 2 gallons of diesel. How much more did your friend pay?

   b. You have $15.24. You buy 3 gallons of gas. How much money do you have left?

   c. The price of gas goes up $0.20 per gallon and the price of diesel goes down $0.14 per gallon. How much more is the price of diesel per gallon than gas?

2.5 Multiplying Decimals
For use with Exploration 2.5

Learning Target: Multiply decimals and solve problems involving multiplication of decimals.

Success Criteria:
- I can multiply decimals by whole numbers.
- I can multiply decimals by decimals.
- I can evaluate expressions involving multiplication of decimals.

1 EXPLORATION: Multiplying Decimals

Work with a partner.

a. Write the multiplication expression represented by each area model. Then find the product. Explain how you found your answer.

i.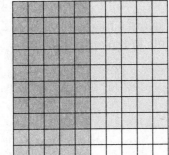

ii.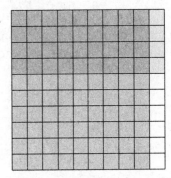

iii.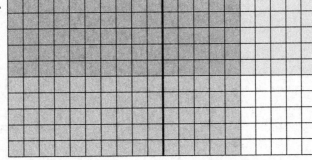

2.5 **Multiplying Decimals** (continued)

iv.

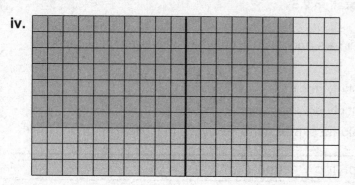

b. How can you find the products in part (a) without using a model?
How do you know where to place the decimal points in the answers?

c. Find the product of 0.55 and 0.45. Explain how you found your answer.

Name_____ Date_____

2.5 Notetaking with Vocabulary

Vocabulary:

Notes:

2.5 Self-Assessment

Use the scale below to rate your understanding of the learning target and the success criteria.

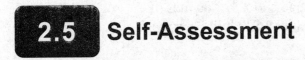

1	2	3	4
I do not understand.	I can do it with help.	I can do it on my own.	I can teach someone else.

	Rating	Date
2.5 Multiplying Decimals		
Learning Target: Multiply decimals and solve problems involving multiplication of decimals.	1 2 3 4	
I can multiply decimals by whole numbers.	1 2 3 4	
I can multiply decimals by decimals.	1 2 3 4	
I can evaluate expressions involving multiplication of decimals.	1 2 3 4	

Name _____ Date _____

1. The weight of an object on the Moon is about 0.167 of its weight on Earth. How much does a 156.5-pound astronaut weigh on the Moon?

2. The table shows the cost (in cents) of producing and distributing each coin for the years 2007 and 2014.

Coin	2007	2014
Quarter	9.78	8.95
Dime	4.09	3.91
Nickel	9.53	8.09
Penny	1.67	1.66

   a. Which coin(s) have a cost in 2014 that is less than 0.95 times the cost in 2007?

   b. How much more did it cost to produce 50 of each coin in 2007 than in 2014?

3. A store is selling sculptures. The first week, it prices 6 sculptures at $80 each. After each week, if a sculpture is not sold, it will be priced to sell for 0.85 times the previous week's price. The store needs to sell the 6 sculptures for a total of $270 to make a profit. What is the last week in which all 6 sculptures could be sold so that the store makes a profit?

4. Which is greater, $7.8 \cdot (6.9 + 3.5)$ or $7.8 + (6.9 \cdot 3.5)$? Explain your answer.

5. When multiplying, how many decimal places are in the product of 1.25^2? 1.25^3? 1.25^4? Explain your reasoning.

6. You buy 3.7 pounds of oranges at $1.99 per pound and 2.425 pounds of pineapple at $2.25 per pound. You hand the cashier a $20 bill. How much change will you receive?

Describe the pattern. Find the next three numbers.

7. 0.7, 2.1, 6.3, 18.9, ...

8. 0.13, 0.65, 3.25, 16.25, ...

9. 2, 0.04, 0.0008, 0.000016, ...

10. 6, 1.8, 0.54, 0.162, ...

11. You are preparing for a trip to Canada. At the time of your trip, each U.S. dollar is worth 1.286 Canadian dollars and each Canadian dollar is worth 0.778 U.S. dollar.

   a. You exchange 180 U.S. dollars for Canadian dollars. How many Canadian dollars do you receive?

   b. You spend 165 Canadian dollars on the trip. Then you exchange the remaining Canadian dollars for U.S. dollars. How many U.S. dollars do you receive?

2.6 Dividing Whole Numbers
For use with Exploration 2.6

Learning Target: Divide whole numbers and solve problems involving division of whole numbers.

Success Criteria:
- I can use long division to divide whole numbers.
- I can write a remainder as a fraction.
- I can interpret quotients in real-life problems.

1 EXPLORATION: Using a Double Bar Graph

Work with a partner. The double bar graph shows the history of a citywide cleanup day.

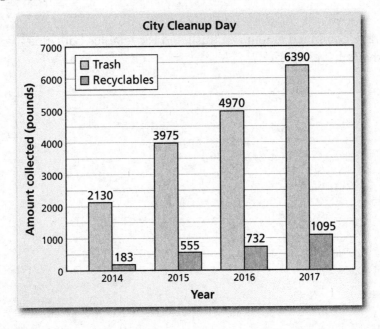

a. Make five conclusions from the graph.

2.6 **Dividing Whole Numbers** (continued)

b. Compare the results of the city cleanup day in 2016 to the results in 2014.

c. What is the average combined amount of trash and recyclables collected each year over the four-year period?

d. Make a prediction about the amount of trash collected in a future year.

Notetaking with Vocabulary

Vocabulary:

Notes:

 **Self-Assessment**

Use the scale below to rate your understanding of the learning target and the success criteria.

1	**2**	**3**	**4**
I do not understand.	I can do it with help.	I can do it on my own.	I can teach someone else.

	Rating	Date
2.6 Dividing Whole Numbers		
Learning Target: Divide whole numbers and solve problems involving division of whole numbers.	1 2 3 4	
I can use long division to divide whole numbers.	1 2 3 4	
I can write a remainder as a fraction.	1 2 3 4	
I can interpret quotients in real-life problems.	1 2 3 4	

2.6 Practice

1. You sign up for 13 weeks of swim lessons. The total cost is $325. What is the cost per week?

2. You have 800 square feet of the room reserved for tables.

   a. Each round table requires 49 square feet. How many round tables will fit in 800 square feet?

   b. Each rectangular table requires 64 square feet. How many rectangular tables will fit in 800 square feet?

   c. The round tables seat 8 people. The rectangular tables seat 12 people. Using your answers in (a) and (b), which type of table will seat more people in the allotted 800 square feet, *round* or *rectangular*?

3. An auditorium seats 48 students per row. A total of 1665 students are in the auditorium today. All the rows are full except for the front row.

   a. How many rows are in the auditorium?

   b. How many students are in the front row?

4. A rectangular room has an area of 120 square feet.

   Area = 120 ft^2

   15 ft

   a. The length of the room is 15 feet. Find the perimeter of the room.

   b. You are laying baseboard along the perimeter of the room. The baseboard comes in 6-foot pieces. Using the perimeter of the room, write an expression for the number of baseboard pieces that are needed for the room. How many baseboard pieces should you buy?

   c. The length of the room is longer than 6 feet. Write an expression to determine how many baseboard pieces are needed for each length of the room. How many baseboard pieces will fit along each length without being cut? How many feet of an additional baseboard piece is needed for each length?

   d. Write an expression to determine how many baseboard pieces are needed for each width of the room. How many baseboard pieces will fit along each width without being cut? How many feet of an additional baseboard piece is needed for each width?

   e. No partial baseboard piece can be less than 2 feet long. Using your answers in (c) and (d), will your answer to part (b) give you enough baseboard pieces? Explain.

2.7 Dividing Decimals
For use with Exploration 2.7

Learning Target: Divide decimals and solve problems involving division of decimals.

Success Criteria:
- • I can divide decimals by whole numbers.
- • I can divide decimals by decimals.
- • I can divide whole numbers by decimals.

1 EXPLORATION: Dividing Decimals

Work with a partner.

   a. Write two division expressions represented by each area model. Then find the quotients. Explain how you found your answer.

    i.

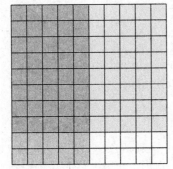

    ii.

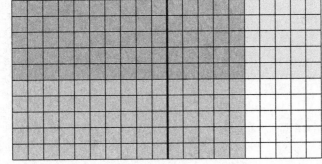

2.7 **Dividing Decimals** (continued)

iii.

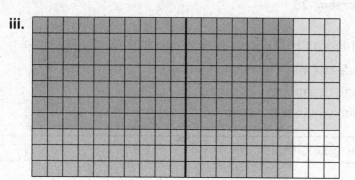

b. Use a calculator to find 119 ÷ 17, 11.9 ÷ 1.7, 1.19 ÷ 0.17, and 0.119 ÷ 0.017. What do you notice? Explain how you can use long division to divide any pair of multi-digit decimals.

2.7 Notetaking with Vocabulary

Vocabulary:

Notes:

2.7 Self-Assessment

Use the scale below to rate your understanding of the learning target and the success criteria.

1	**2**	**3**	**4**
I do not understand.	I can do it with help.	I can do it on my own.	I can teach someone else.

	Rating	Date
2.7 Dividing Decimals		
Learning Target: Divide decimals and solve problems involving division of decimals.	1 2 3 4	
I can divide decimals by whole numbers.	1 2 3 4	
I can divide decimals by decimals.	1 2 3 4	
I can divide whole numbers by decimals.	1 2 3 4	

2.7 Practice

1. The table shows the ounces and costs of three boxes of the same cereal. Which box of cereal is the best buy? Explain.

Ounces	Cost
12	$2.88
18	$3.96
28	$6.44

2. A person's walking stride is about 0.413 times the person's height in inches. Your friend's stride is 27.258 inches. How tall is your friend in feet?

3. Write $2.7 \div 9$ as a multiplication problem with a missing factor.

4. You are saving your money to buy a guitar that costs $275.75. You have $40 and plan to save $7.50 each week. Your uncle decides to give you an additional $8 each week.

   a. How many weeks will you have to save until you have enough money to buy the guitar?

   b. How many more weeks would you have to save to buy a guitar that costs $339.75? Explain how you found your answer.

Without finding the quotient, complete the statement using <, >, or =. Explain your reasoning.

5. $4.58 \div 0.57$ _____ $45.8 \div 0.57$

6. $24.5 \div 0.4$ _____ $24.5 \div 4$

7. Your parent competes in an Ironman competition. The table shows the finish times, in minutes, for each portion of the competition.

Swim	76.28
Bike	384.12
Run	265.29

   a. The swim course is 2.4 miles long. The bike course is 112 miles long. How many times greater is the miles per hour for the bike portion than the swim portion?

   b. The run course is 26.2 miles long. What is the overall miles per hour for the Ironman competition?

   c. Ironman competitions count transition times between the swim and the bike, and the bike and the run. The recorded overall miles per hour was 11.53 miles per hour. How many minutes did your parent spend in transition?

Name_____ Date_____

Chapter Self-Assessment

Use the scale below to rate your understanding of the learning target and the success criteria.

1 I do not understand. **2** I can do it with help. **3** I can do it on my own. **4** I can teach someone else.

	Rating	Date
2.1 Multiplying Fractions		
Learning Target: Find products involving fractions and mixed numbers.	1 2 3 4	
I can draw a model to explain fraction multiplication.	1 2 3 4	
I can multiply fractions.	1 2 3 4	
I can find products involving mixed numbers.	1 2 3 4	
I can interpret products involving fractions and mixed numbers to solve real-life problems.	1 2 3 4	
2.2 Dividing Fractions		
Learning Target: Compute quotients of fractions and solve problems involving division by fractions.	1 2 3 4	
I can draw a model to explain division of fractions.	1 2 3 4	
I can find reciprocals of numbers.	1 2 3 4	
I can divide fractions by fractions.	1 2 3 4	
I can divide fractions and whole numbers.	1 2 3 4	
2.3 Dividing Mixed Numbers		
Learning Target: Compute quotients with mixed numbers and solve problems involving division with mixed numbers.	1 2 3 4	
I can draw a model to explain division of mixed numbers.	1 2 3 4	
I can write a mixed number as an improper fraction.	1 2 3 4	
I can divide with mixed numbers.	1 2 3 4	
I can evaluate expressions involving mixed numbers using the order of operations.	1 2 3 4	

Name _____ Date _____

	Rating	Date
2.4 Adding and Subtracting Decimals		
Learning Target: Add and subtract decimals and solve problems involving addition and subtraction of decimals.	1 2 3 4	
I can explain why it is necessary to line up the decimal points when adding and subtracting decimals.	1 2 3 4	
I can add decimals.	1 2 3 4	
I can subtract decimals.	1 2 3 4	
I can evaluate expressions involving addition and subtraction of decimals.	1 2 3 4	
2.5 Multiplying Decimals		
Learning Target: Multiply decimals and solve problems involving multiplication of decimals.	1 2 3 4	
I can multiply decimals by whole numbers.	1 2 3 4	
I can multiply decimals by decimals.	1 2 3 4	
I can evaluate expressions involving multiplication of decimals.	1 2 3 4	
2.6 Dividing Whole Numbers		
Learning Target: Divide whole numbers and solve problems involving division of whole numbers.	1 2 3 4	
I can use long division to divide whole numbers.	1 2 3 4	
I can write a remainder as a fraction.	1 2 3 4	
I can interpret quotients in real-life problems.	1 2 3 4	
2.7 Dividing Decimals		
Learning Target: Divide decimals and solve problems involving division of decimals.	1 2 3 4	
I can divide decimals by whole numbers.	1 2 3 4	
I can divide decimals by decimals.	1 2 3 4	
I can divide whole numbers by decimals.	1 2 3 4	

Name_____ Date _____

Using the numbers from the table, find and state the rule in words.

1.

x	y
1	4
2	5
3	6
4	7

2.

x	y
2	6
4	12
6	18
8	24

3.

x	y
12	2
24	14
36	26
48	38

4.

x	y
4	2
5	$\frac{5}{2}$
6	3
7	$\frac{7}{2}$

5. The table shows the results of buying pretzels from a vending machine. The x column is the amount you put into the machine. The y column is the change you receive back from the machine. Complete the table and state the rule in words.

x	y
0.65	0
0.70	0.05
0.75	0.10
1.00	

Name_____ Date _____

Simplify the expression.

6. $\dfrac{5}{9} \cdot \dfrac{1}{3}$

7. $\dfrac{8}{15} \cdot \dfrac{3}{4}$

8. $\dfrac{1}{8} \cdot \dfrac{1}{9}$

9. $\dfrac{2}{3} \div \dfrac{9}{10}$

10. $\dfrac{7}{8} \div \dfrac{11}{16}$

11. $\dfrac{3}{10} \div \dfrac{2}{5}$

12. You have 8 cups of flour. A recipe calls for $\dfrac{2}{3}$ cup of flour. Another recipe calls for $\dfrac{1}{4}$ cup of flour. How much flour do you have left after making the recipes?

Ratios

For use with Exploration 3.1

Learning Target: Understand the concepts of ratios and equivalent ratios.

Success Criteria:
- I can write and interpret ratios using appropriate notation and language.
- I can recognize multiplicative relationships in ratios.
- I can describe how to determine whether ratios are equivalent.
- I can name ratios equivalent to a given ratio.

A **ratio** is a comparison of two quantities. Consider two quantities a and b. The ratio $a : b$ indicates that there are a units of the first quantity for every b units of the second quantity.

1 EXPLORATION: Writing Ratios

Work with a partner. A science class has two times as many girls as it has boys.

a. Discuss possible numbers of boys and girls in the science class.

b. What comparisons can you make between your class and the science class? Can you determine which class has more girls? More boys? Explain your reasoning?

c. Write three ratios that you observe in your classroom. Describe what each ratio represents.

Name _____ Date _____

3.1 Ratios (continued)

2 **EXPLORATION:** Using Ratios in a Recipe

**Work with a partner. The ratio of iced tea to lemonade in a recipe is 3 : 1.
You begin by combining 3 cups of iced tea with 1 cup of lemonade.**

Iced Tea   Lemonade

a. You add 1 cup of iced tea and 1 cup of lemonade to the mixture. Does this
change the taste of the mixture?

b. Describe how you can make larger amounts without changing the taste.

Name_____ Date_____

 Notetaking with Vocabulary

Vocabulary:

Notes:

 Self-Assessment

Use the scale below to rate your understanding of the learning target and the success criteria.

1	2	3	4
I do not understand.	I can do it with help.	I can do it on my own.	I can teach someone else.

	Rating	Date
3.1 Ratios		
Learning Target: Understand the concepts of ratios and equivalent ratios.	1 2 3 4	
I can write and interpret ratios using appropriate notation and language.	1 2 3 4	
I can recognize multiplicative relationships in ratios.	1 2 3 4	
I can describe how to determine whether ratios are equivalent.	1 2 3 4	
I can name ratios equivalent to a given ratio.	1 2 3 4	

Name_____ Date _____

3.1 Practice

Write the ratio. Explain what the ratio means.

1. circles to triangles

2. triangles to circles

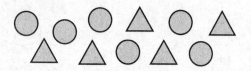 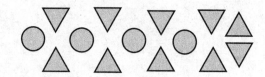

Fill in the blank so that the ratios are equivalent.

3. 4 : 7 and 12 : ___

4. ___ : 18 and 5 : 3

5. In a recipe for tomato sauce, the ratio of fluid ounces of water to fluid ounces of tomato paste is 3 : 4. You plan to make 35 fluid ounces of tomato sauce. How many fluid ounces of tomato paste do you need?

6. A middle school band has 45 sixth and seventh graders. The ratio of sixth graders to seventh graders is 2 to 3. How many sixth graders are in the band? Explain how you got your answer.

7. The ratio of the ages (in years) of three children is 2 : 4 : 5. The sum of their ages is 33. What is the age of each child?

8. You make a necklace using blue, purple, and green beads in a ratio of 1 : 1 : 2. You use a total of 168 beads. How many green beads are in the necklace?

9. A caterer makes 3 extra sandwiches for every 20 sandwiches a customer orders.

   a. Write the ratio of ordered sandwiches to extra sandwiches.

   b. Write the ratio of total sandwiches to ordered sandwiches.

   c. The caterer makes a total of 184 sandwiches for a customer. How many sandwiches did the customer order?

10. The ratio of girls to boys in your class is 5 to 7. Two girls joined your class. Now the ratio of girls to boys is 6 to 7. How many students are now in your class? Explain how you got your answer.

Name_____ Date_____

 Using Tape Diagrams
3.2 For use with Exploration 3.2

Learning Target: Use tape diagrams to model and solve ratio problems.

Success Criteria:
- I can interpret tape diagrams that represent ratio relationships.
- I can draw tape diagrams to model ratio relationships.
- I can find the value of one part of a tape diagram.
- I can use tape diagrams to solve ratio problems.

You can use a visual model, called a *tape diagram*, to represent the relationship between two quantities in a ratio.

1 EXPLORATION: Using a Tape Diagram

Work with a partner. The tape diagram models the lengths of two snowboarding trails.

Beginner Trail [ ]

Expert Trail [| | |]

a. What can you determine from the tape diagram?

b. Choose a length for one of the trails. What conclusions can you make from the tape diagram? Explain your reasoning?

3.2 **Using Tape Diagrams** (continued)

c. Suppose you know the combined length of the trails or the difference in the lengths of the trails. Explain how you can use that information to find the lengths of the two trails. Provide an example with your explanation.

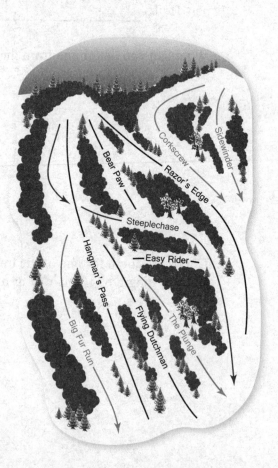

3.2 Notetaking with Vocabulary

Vocabulary:

Notes:

3.2 Self-Assessment

Use the scale below to rate your understanding of the learning target and the success criteria.

1	2	3	4
I do not understand.	I can do it with help.	I can do it on my own.	I can teach someone else.

	Rating	Date
3.2 Using Tape Diagrams		
Learning Target: Use tape diagrams to model and solve ratio problems.	1 2 3 4	
I can interpret tape diagrams that represent ratio relationships.	1 2 3 4	
I can draw tape diagrams to model ratio relationships.	1 2 3 4	
I can find the value of one part of a tape diagram.	1 2 3 4	
I can use tape diagrams to solve ratio problems.	1 2 3 4	

Practice

You and a friend tutor a total of 18 hours. Use the tape diagram to find how many hours you tutor.

1. You:

Friend:

2. You:

Friend:

A bowl contains blackberries and raspberries. You are given the total number of berries in the bowl and ratio of blackberries to raspberries. How many of each berry are in the bowl?

3. 15 berries; 1 to 4

4. 24 berries; 5 for every 3

5. 54 berries; 2 : 7

6. 48 berries; 13 for every 11

7. There are 12 more cars than trucks in a parking garage. The ratio of trucks to cars is 3 : 5. How many trucks and how many cars are in the parking garage?

8. You separate a large bag of baby carrots into two groups: one for your lunchbox and one for your friend's lunchbox. The tape diagram represents the ratio of small bags of baby carrots for your lunchbox to small bags of baby carrots for your friend's lunchbox. Each small bag contains 7 baby carrots. You make 8 small bags of baby carrots for your lunchbox.

You:

Friend:

a. How many small bags of baby carrots did you make for your friend's lunchbox?

b. How many baby carrots are in the large bag of baby carrots?

Using Ratio Tables
For use with Exploration 3.3

Learning Target: Use ratio tables to represent equivalent ratios and solve ratio problems.

Success Criteria:
- I can use various operations to create tables of equivalent ratios.
- I can use ratio tables to solve ratio problems.
- I can use ratio tables to compare ratios.

 EXPLORATION: Making a Table of Equivalent Ratios

Work with a partner. You buy milk that contains 180 calories per 2 cups.

    a. You measure 2 cups of the milk for a recipe and pour it into a pitcher. You repeat this four more times. Make a table to show the numbers of calories and cups in the pitcher as you add the milk.

    b. Describe any relationships you see in your table.

    c. Describe ways that you can find equivalent ratios using different operations.

3.3 **Using Ratio Tables** (continued)

2 **EXPLORATION:** Creating a Double Number Line

Work with a partner.

a. Represent the ratio in Exploration 1 by labeling the increments on the *double number line* below. Can you label the increments in more than one way?

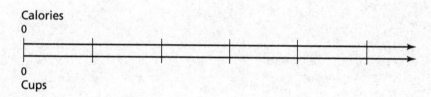

Calories
0

0
Cups

b. How can you use the double number line to find the number of calories in 3 cups of milk? 3.5 cups of milk?

Notetaking with Vocabulary

Vocabulary:

Notes:

 **Self-Assessment**

Use the scale below to rate your understanding of the learning target and the success criteria.

1	2	3	4
I do not understand.	I can do it with help.	I can do it on my own.	I can teach someone else.

	Rating	Date
3.3 Using Ratio Tables		
Learning Target: Use ratio tables to represent equivalent ratios and solve ratio problems.	1 2 3 4	
I can use various operations to create tables of equivalent ratios.	1 2 3 4	
I can use ratio tables to solve ratio problems.	1 2 3 4	
I can use ratio tables to compare ratios.	1 2 3 4	

3.3 Practice

Complete the ratio table to solve the problem.

1. You baked 42 chocolate cupcakes and 28 red velvet cupcakes. You package them in boxes that have the same ratio of chocolate to red velvet as the total cupcakes. How many red velvet cupcakes are in a box that has 24 chocolate cupcakes?

Chocolate	Red Velvet
42	28
24	

2. The number of free song downloads is determined using a ratio. When you purchase 40 songs, you get 24 free song downloads. How many songs must you purchase in order to get 18 free song downloads?

Purchase	Free
40	24
	18

3. Describe and correct the error in making the ratio table.

A	B
64	32
56	24
48	16

Two whole numbers *A* and *B* satisfy the following conditions. Find *A* and *B*.

4. $A + B = 32$

   $A : B$ is equivalent to $5 : 11$

5. $A + B = 76$

   $A : B$ is equivalent to $14 : 5$

6. $A - B = 56$

   $A : B$ is equivalent to $9 : 2$

7. $A - B = 65$

   $A : B$ is equivalent to $20 : 7$

8. You and a friend have a hula hoop competition. You win 3 out of every 7 trials. Your friend wins 5 more trials than you. How many trials are in the competition?

3.4 **Graphing Ratio Relationships**
For use with Exploration 3.4

Learning Target: Represent ratio relationships in a coordinate plane.

Success Criteria: • I can create and plot ordered pairs from a ratio relationship.
• I can create graphs to solve ratio problems.
• I can create graphs to compare ratios.

1 **EXPLORATION: Using a Coordinate Plane**

Work with a partner. An airplane travels 300 miles per hour.

a. Represent the relationship between distance and time in a coordinate plane.
Explain your choice for labeling and scaling the axes.

b. Write a question that can be answered using the graph. Exchange your
question with another group. Answer their question and discuss the solution
with the other group.

Big Ideas Math: Modeling Real Life Grade 6 **71**
Student Journal

3.4 **Graphing Ratio Relationships** (continued)

2 **EXPLORATION:** Identifying Relationships in Graphs

Work with a partner. Use the graphs to make a ratio table. Explain how the black, gray, and dashed arrows correspond to the ratio table.

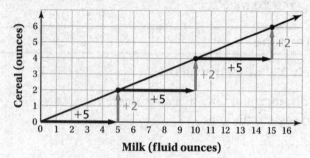

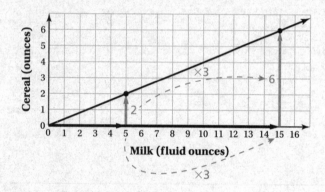

Name_____ Date_____

Notetaking with Vocabulary

Vocabulary:

Notes:

Self-Assessment

Use the scale below to rate your understanding of the learning target and the success criteria.

1	2	3	4
I do not understand.	I can do it with help.	I can do it on my own.	I can teach someone else.

	Rating	Date
3.4 Graphing Ratio Relationships		
Learning Target: Represent ratio relationships in a coordinate plane.	1 2 3 4	
I can create and plot ordered pairs from a ratio relationship.	1 2 3 4	
I can create graphs to solve ratio problems.	1 2 3 4	
I can create graphs to compare ratios.	1 2 3 4	

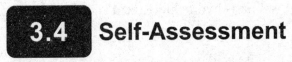

3.4 Practice

1. Your school is selling local coupon books as a fundraiser for more computers in the library. The school earns $4.50 for every coupon book sold.

   a. Represent the ratio relationship using a graph.

   b. How much money does your school earn if 9 coupon books are sold?

2. Just by looking at the graph, determine whose paint has a darker orange color. Explain.

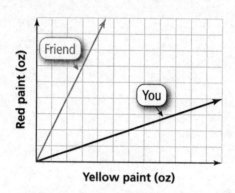

3. Your friend drinks 6 eight-ounce glasses of water every 5 hours. You drink 8 eight-ounce glasses of water every 7 hours. Graph each ratio relationship in the same coordinate plane. Who drinks water faster, you or your friend?

4. A chemist prepares two acid solutions. The first solution is 2 parts hydrochloric acid for every 5 parts water. The second solution is 3 parts hydrochloric acid for every 7 parts water.

   a. Use a ratio table to determine which solution is more acidic.

   b. Use a graph to determine which solution is more acidic.

   c. Which method do you prefer? Explain.

5. You made a lemonade tea mixture with 2 cups of lemonade for every 5 cups of tea. Your friend made a lemonade tea mixture with 5 cups of lemonade for every 9 cups of tea, using the same size container.

   a. How many cups of lemonade tea mixture are in the smallest possible container?

   b. Graph each ratio relationship. What can you conclude?

   c. Which tea has a more sour taste, yours or your friend's? Explain your reasoning.

3.5 Rates and Unit Rates
For use with Exploration 3.5

Learning Target: Understand the concept of a unit rate and solve rate problems.

Success Criteria:
- I can find unit rates.
- I can use unit rates to solve rate problems.
- I can use unit rates to compare rates.

1 EXPLORATION: Using a Diagram

Work with a partner. The diagram shows a story problem.

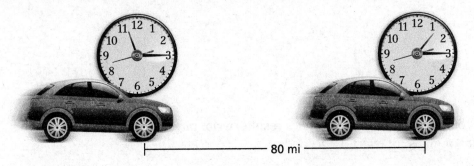

          |——————— 80 mi ———————|

a. What information can you obtain from the diagram?

b. Assuming that the car travels at a constant speed, how far does the car travel in 3.25 hours? Explain your method.

c. Draw a speedometer that shows the speed of the car. How can you use the speedometer to answer part (b)?

3.5 **Rates and Unit Rates** (continued)

2 **EXPLORATION:** Using Equivalent Ratios

> **Work with a partner. Count the number of times you can clap your hands in 12 seconds. Have your partner record your results. Then switch roles with your partner and repeat the process.**

a. Using your results and your partner's results, write ratios that represent the numbers of claps for every 12 seconds.

b. Explain how you can use the ratios in part (a) to find the numbers of times you and your partner can clasp your hands in 2 minutes, in 2.5 minutes, and in 3 minutes.

Name_____ Date_____

 3.5 Notetaking with Vocabulary

Vocabulary:

Notes:

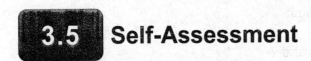 **3.5** Self-Assessment

Use the scale below to rate your understanding of the learning target and the success criteria.

1	**2**	**3**	**4**
I do not understand.	I can do it with help.	I can do it on my own.	I can teach someone else.

	Rating	Date
3.5 Rates and Unit Rates		
Learning Target: Understand the concept of a unit rate and solve rate problems.	1 2 3 4	
I can find unit rates.	1 2 3 4	
I can use unit rates to solve rate problems.	1 2 3 4	
I can use unit rates to compare rates.	1 2 3 4	

Name _____ Date _____

Find the missing values in the ratio table.

1.

Feet	12		
Seconds	5	1	9

2.

Dollars	20	1	23
Hour	3		

3. An aquarium is leaking water at a rate of three quarts in 4 days.

   a. How many quarts are leaked in 1 week?

   b. How many days does it take for 9 quarts to leak out of the aquarium?

Decide whether the rates are equivalent.

4. 35 kilometers in 25 minutes,

   14 kilometers in 10 minutes

5. 25 minutes for $3,

   1 hour for $6

6. You are researching two glaciers. The first glacier flows at a rate of 75 meters in 3 days. The second glacier flows at a rate of 107.5 meters in 5 days. Which glacier flows faster? How much sooner will the faster glacier flow 200 meters?

7. A teacher keeps track of how many books are read by students in each class. Which grade has read a higher rate of books per student? How many books does the other grade need to read to have the same rate?

	Grade 6		Grade 7	
	Class A	Class B	Class C	Class D
Students	25	31	21	23
Books Read	181	155	116	126

8. Charles Lindbergh made the first solo airplane flight from New York to Paris. His flight covered about 3610 miles in 33.5 hours.

   a. Find the unit rate in miles per hour.

   b. Find the unit rate in hours per mile.

   c. Which is a better description of Lindbergh's rate, *about two miles per minute* or *about two minutes per mile*? Explain your reasoning.

3.6 Converting Measures
For use with Exploration 3.6

Learning Target: Use ratio reasoning to convert units of measure.

Success Criteria:
- I can write conversion facts as unit rates.
- I can convert units of measure using ratio tables.
- I can convert units of measure using conversion factors.
- I can convert rates using conversion factors.

---

1 **EXPLORATION:** Estimating Unit Conversions

Work with a partner. You are given 4 one-liter containers and a one-gallon container.

a. A full one-gallon container can be used to fill the one-liter containers, as shown below. Write a unit rate that estimates the number of liters per gallon.

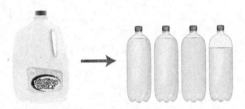

b. A full one-liter container can be used to partially fill the one-gallon container, as shown below. Write a unit rate that estimates the number of gallons per liter.

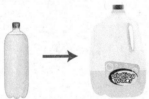

c. Estimate the number of liters in 5.5 gallons and the number of gallons in 12 liters. What method(s) did you use? What other methods could you have used?

3.6 **Converting Measures** (continued)

2 **EXPLORATION:** Converting Units in a Rate

Work with a partner. The rate that a caterpillar moves is given in inches per minute. Using the rulers below, how can you convert the rate to centimeters per second? Justify your answer.

Notetaking with Vocabulary

Vocabulary:

Notes:

 Self-Assessment

Use the scale below to rate your understanding of the learning target and the success criteria.

1	2	3	4
I do not understand.	I can do it with help.	I can do it on my own.	I can teach someone else.

	Rating	Date
3.6 Converting Measures		
Learning Target: Use ratio reasoning to convert units of measure.	1 2 3 4	
I can write conversion facts as unit rates.	1 2 3 4	
I can convert units of measure using ratio tables.	1 2 3 4	
I can convert units of measure using conversion factors.	1 2 3 4	
I can convert rates using conversion factors.	1 2 3 4	

3.6 Practice

1. Your cat weighs 10.4 pounds. How many kilograms does your cat weigh?

Complete the statement using < or >.

2. 29 ft ____ 880 cm

3. 10 pt ____ 5 L

4. 42 km ____ 26.2 mi

5. 350 g ____ 12 oz

Complete the statement.

6. $\dfrac{42 \text{ gal}}{\text{min}} \approx \dfrac{\underline{\quad} \text{ L}}{\text{min}}$

7. $\dfrac{32 \text{ ft}}{\text{sec}} \approx \dfrac{\underline{\quad} \text{ m}}{\text{sec}}$

8. $\dfrac{15 \text{ kg}}{\text{yr}} \approx \dfrac{\underline{\quad} \text{ oz}}{\text{yr}}$

9. $\dfrac{5.7 \text{ km}}{\text{h}} \approx \dfrac{\underline{\quad} \text{ ft}}{\text{h}}$

10. At the equator, Earth's surface moves about 40,000 kilometers per day.

   a. What is this speed in miles per hour?

   b. What is this speed in meters per minute?

   c. You stand at a place 200 miles north of the equator. Are you moving *more than* or *less than* 40,000 kilometers per day?

11. Your car's gasoline tank holds 18 gallons of gasoline. On a trip in Canada, the tank is one quarter full. You want to fill the tank. How many liters of gasoline are needed to fill the tank? Explain your answer.

12. You can swim 25 meters in 0.4 minutes.

   a. What is your pace in seconds per meter?

   b. What is your pace in yards per second?

   c. Your friend swims at a pace of 2.3 miles per hour. Who swims faster, *you* or *your friend*?

13. One gallon of paint covers 350 square feet.

   a. How many liters of paint does it take to cover a room whose walls have an area of 1000 square meters?

   b. The store only had enough liters of paint to cover an area of 600 square meters. You purchased the remaining paint in quart-size containers. How many quarts of paint did you buy to cover the remaining area of 400 square meters?

Name_____ Date _____

Chapter 3 Chapter Self-Assessment

Use the scale below to rate your understanding of the learning target and the success criteria.

1	*2*	*3*	*4*
I do not understand.	I can do it with help.	I can do it on my own.	I can teach someone else.

	Rating	Date
3.1 Ratios		
Learning Target: Understand the concepts of ratios and equivalent ratios.	1 2 3 4	
I can write and interpret ratios using appropriate notation and language.	1 2 3 4	
I can recognize multiplicative relationships in ratios.	1 2 3 4	
I can describe how to determine whether ratios are equivalent.	1 2 3 4	
I can name ratios equivalent to a given ratio.	1 2 3 4	
3.2 Using Tape Diagrams		
Learning Target: Use tape diagrams to model and solve ratio problems.	1 2 3 4	
I can interpret tape diagrams that represent ratio relationships.	1 2 3 4	
I can draw tape diagrams to model ratio relationships.	1 2 3 4	
I can find the value of one part of a tape diagram.	1 2 3 4	
I can use tape diagrams to solve ratio problems.	1 2 3 4	
3.3 Using Ratio Tables		
Learning Target: Use ratio tables to represent equivalent ratios and solve ratio problems.	1 2 3 4	
I can use various operations to create tables of equivalent ratios.	1 2 3 4	
I can use ratio tables to solve ratio problems.	1 2 3 4	
I can use ratio tables to compare ratios.	1 2 3 4	

Chapter 3 Chapter Self-Assessment (continued)

	Rating	Date
3.4 Graphing Ratio Relationships		
Learning Target: Represent ratio relationships in a coordinate plane.	1 2 3 4	
I can create and plot ordered pairs from a ratio relationship.	1 2 3 4	
I can create graphs to solve ratio problems.	1 2 3 4	
I can create graphs to compare ratios.	1 2 3 4	
3.5 Rates and Unit Rates		
Learning Target: Understand the concept of a unit rate and solve rate problems.	1 2 3 4	
I can find unit rates.	1 2 3 4	
I can use unit rates to solve rate problems.	1 2 3 4	
I can use unit rates to compare rates.	1 2 3 4	
3.6 Converting Measures		
Learning Target: Use ratio reasoning to convert units of measure.	1 2 3 4	
I can write conversion facts as unit rates.	1 2 3 4	
I can convert units of measure using ratio tables.	1 2 3 4	
I can convert units of measure using conversion factors.	1 2 3 4	
I can convert rates using conversion factors.	1 2 3 4	

Chapter 4 Review & Refresh

Use a number line to order the numbers from least to greatest.

1. 0.2, 0.54, 0.61, 0.4

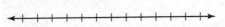

2. 0.3, 0.45, 0.11, 0.02

3. 1.7, 1.24, 1.02, 1.33

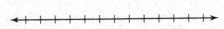

4. 1.01, 1.42, 1.06, 1.2

5. 0.98, 1.23, 0.87, 0.9

6. 1.4, 0.06, 1.23, 0.5

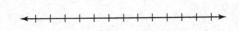

7. 0.003, 0.03, 0.033, 0.031

8. 0.2, 0.002, 0.02, 0.022

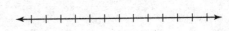

9. In your class, 0.58 of the students bring a piece of whole fruit for a snack and 0.36 of the students bring a snack pack of crackers. Which group of students brings in more food items for a snack?

Name_____ Date _____

Complete the number sentence with <, >, or =.

10. 5 ___ 8

11. 13 ___ 9

12. 0.3 ___ $\frac{3}{8}$

13. 0.68 ___ $\frac{17}{25}$

14. 3.6 ___ $\frac{12}{5}$

15. 0.06 ___ 0.062

Find three numbers that make the number sentence true.

16. $0.35 <$ ___

17. $\frac{4}{9} <$ ___

18. $2\frac{3}{5} \leq$ ___

19. $\frac{1}{10} <$ ___

20. $0.485 \geq$ ___

21. $5.87 \leq$ ___

22. During a trivia game, you answered 18 out of 25 questions correctly. Your friend answered 0.7 of the questions correctly. Write a number sentence for who had the greater number of correct answers.

4.1 Percents and Fractions
For use with Exploration 4.1

Learning Target: Write percents as fractions and fractions as percents.

Success Criteria:
- I can draw models to represent fractions and percents.
- I can write percents as fractions.
- I can write equivalent fractions with denominators of 100.
- I can write fractions as percents.

1 EXPLORATION: Interpreting Models

Work with a partner. Write a percent, a fraction, and a ratio shown by each model. How are percents, fractions, and ratios related?

a.

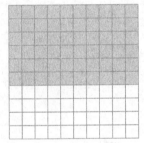

b.

4.1 Percents and Fractions (continued)

1 EXPLORATION: Interpreting Models

Work with a partner. Write a percent, a fraction, and a ratio shown by each model. How are percents, fractions, and ratios related?

c.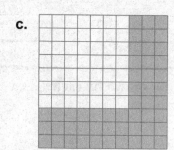

d.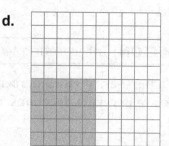

4.1 Notetaking with Vocabulary

Vocabulary:

Notes:

4.1 Self-Assessment

Use the scale below to rate your understanding of the learning target and the success criteria.

1	2	3	4
I do not understand.	I can do it with help.	I can do it on my own.	I can teach someone else.

	Rating	Date
4.1 Percents and Fractions		
Learning Target: Write percents as fractions and fractions as percents.	1 2 3 4	
I can draw models to represent fractions and percents.	1 2 3 4	
I can write percents as fractions.	1 2 3 4	
I can write equivalent fractions with denominators of 100.	1 2 3 4	
I can write fractions as percents.	1 2 3 4	

Name_____ Date _____

Practice

Write the percent as a fraction or mixed number in simplest form.

1. 81.4%   **2.** 210%   **3.** 0.8%   **4.** 0.0125%

Write the fraction or mixed number as a percent.

5. $3\frac{1}{4}$ **6.** $2\frac{1}{2}$ **7.** $1\frac{4}{5}$ **8.** $5\frac{7}{50}$

9. On a school bus, 22 of the 40 students are seated in window seats, and the rest are seated in aisle seats.

    a. What fraction of the students are seated in window seats?

    b. What percent of the students are seated in aisle seats?

    c. More students get on the bus and the percent of students seated in window seats is now 50%. What is the minimum number of students that could have gotten on the bus? Explain your answer.

10. The United States Flag is actually 105% as tall as the state flag of Florida. Write this percent as a mixed number and explain why the perspective in the figure may be misleading.

11. At a zoo, an anaconda is 118% as long as a Burmese python and $1\frac{3}{20}$ times as long as a reticulated python. Which is longer, the Burmese python or the reticulated python? Explain.

12. Draw another square with sides that are $\frac{1}{2}$ as long as the sides of the given square. What percent of the area of the original square is the area of the smaller square?

13. The weight of a tree is doubling every 3 years. In how many years will the weight of the tree be 1600% of its weight now?

Name_____ Date _____

4.2 **Percents and Decimals**
For use with Exploration 4.2

Learning Target: Write percents as decimals and decimals as percents.

Success Criteria:
- I can draw models to represent decimals.
- I can explain why the decimal point moves when multiplying and dividing by 100.
- I can write percents as decimals.
- I can write decimals as percents.

1 **EXPLORATION:** Interpreting Models

Work with a partner. Write a percent and a decimal shown by each model. How are percents and decimals related?

a.
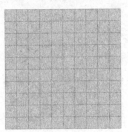

b.
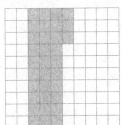

c.
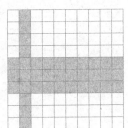

d.
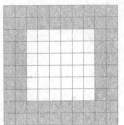

4.2 **Percents and Decimals** (continued)

e.

f.
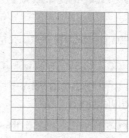

g.
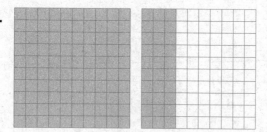

Name_____ Date_____

 Notetaking with Vocabulary

Vocabulary:

Notes:

 Self-Assessment

Use the scale below to rate your understanding of the learning target and the success criteria.

1	2	3	4
I do not understand.	I can do it with help.	I can do it on my own.	I can teach someone else.

	Rating	Date
4.2 Percents and Decimals		
Learning Target: Write percents as decimals and decimals as percents.	1 2 3 4	
I can draw models to represent decimals.	1 2 3 4	
I can explain why the decimal point moves when multiplying and dividing by 100.	1 2 3 4	
I can write percents as decimals.	1 2 3 4	
I can write decimals as percents.	1 2 3 4	

4.2 Practice

Write the percent as a fraction in simplest form and as a decimal.

1. 42.4%   2. 73.6%   3. 31.25%   4. 44.65%

5. About 0.36 of the students at a middle school are seventh graders.

 a. What fraction of the students at the middle school are not seventh graders?

 b. There are equal numbers of sixth and eighth graders at the middle school. What percent of the students at the middle school are sixth graders?

6. The percents of three types of tickets collected at the gate for a high school football game are shown.

Ticket type	Student	Adult	Senior (65 and older)
Percent	48%	28%	14%

 a. Write the percents as decimals and as fractions.

 b. There is one other type of ticket that is not shown. It is a ticket for a child under 5. What percent of the tickets were of this type?

7. Students in an after-school enrichment program chose one of five subject areas.

 a. What percent chose English or reading?

 b. What percent chose math? Write the percent as a decimal.

 c. The after-school enrichment program stopped offering the History program. Half of the students in the History program went to the Art program, and the remaining students equally chose the remaining three programs. What are the new percents for Art, Math, Reading and English? Write the percents as decimals.

Subject Chosen

Art 26%
Math ?
History 14%
Reading 0.12
English 0.21

8. At one school, half of the students live within one mile, 78% live within 2 miles, and 0.1 of the students live between 2 and 3 miles from the school. Make a table to show the percent of students who live at each distance from the school.

 a. within 1 mile   b. between 1 and 2 miles

 c. between 2 and 3 miles   d. more than 3 miles

**Comparing and Ordering
Fractions, Decimals, and Percents**
For use with Exploration 4.3

Learning Target: Compare and order fractions, decimals, and percents.

Success Criteria:
- I can rewrite a group of fractions, decimals, and percents using the same representation.
- I can explain how to compare fractions, decimals, and percents.
- I can order fractions, decimals, and percents from least to greatest.

1 **EXPLORATION:** Using a Number Line to Order Numbers

Work with three partners. Create a number line on the floor. Have your group stand on the number line to represent the four numbers in each list. Use the results to order each list of numbers from least to greatest. How did you know where to stand?

a.

0.25	0.9%	40%	0.5

b.

0%	$\frac{3}{4}$	30%	$\frac{1}{20}$

4.3 **Comparing and Ordering Fractions, Decimals, and Percents** (continued)

c.

100%	0.125	75%	$\dfrac{3}{10}$

d.

12.5%	1.02	$\dfrac{1}{100}$	25%

e.

0.3	$\dfrac{1}{8}$	4%	0.75

f.

$\dfrac{51}{50}$	105%	1.5	$\dfrac{9}{10}$

Name_____ Date_____

4.3 Notetaking with Vocabulary

Vocabulary:

Notes:

4.3 Self-Assessment

Use the scale below to rate your understanding of the learning target and the success criteria.

1	**2**	**3**	**4**
I do not understand.	I can do it with help.	I can do it on my own.	I can teach someone else.

	Rating	Date
4.3 Comparing and Ordering Fractions, Decimals, and Percents		
Learning Target: Compare and order fractions, decimals, and percents.	1 2 3 4	
I can rewrite a group of fractions, decimals, and percents using the same representation.	1 2 3 4	
I can explain how to compare fractions, decimals, and percents.	1 2 3 4	
I can order fractions, decimals, and percents from least to greatest.	1 2 3 4	

Name _____ Date _____

Practice 4.3

Use a number line to order the numbers from least to greatest.

1. $\frac{1}{3}$, 0.3, 33%, $\frac{8}{25}$, 33.6%

2. 210%, 2.2, $2.\overline{2}$, $\frac{43}{20}$

Tell which letter shows the graph of the number.

3. 0.884

4. $\frac{8}{9}$

5. $\frac{22}{25}$

6. 0.89

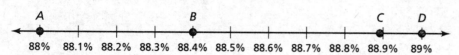

7. Describe a process that you can use to find a decimal whose value is between 31% and 32%.

8. Is 6 centimeters greater than 5% of a meter? Explain.

9. Does 6% of a pound weigh more than an ounce? Explain.

10. Order the periods of time from least to greatest.

   1% of an hour $\frac{2}{3}$ of a minute   0.0004 of a day

11. The table shows the portions of the U.S. population that lived in Florida in certain years.

Year	1860	1910	1960	2010
Portion of U.S. Population In Florida	0.45%	0.0082	$\frac{1}{36}$	$\frac{1}{16}$

   a. Order the portions from least to greatest.

   b. Since 1860, how has the population of Florida increased compared to the population of the United States? Why do you think this happened?

   c. Do you think what you described in part (b) will always happen? Explain your reasoning.

12. Arsenic is toxic to humans. The greatest amount of arsenic that is allowed in drinking water is 10 parts per billion. A test shows that a source of drinking water contains 0.000002% arsenic. Is this an allowable amount? Explain.

Name_____ Date _____

4.4 Solving Percent Problems
For use with Exploration 4.4

Learning Target: Find a percent of a quantity and solve percent problems.

Success Criteria:
- I can represent percents of numbers using an equation, a ratio table, or a model.
- I can find percents of numbers.
- I can find the whole given a part and the percent.

1 EXPLORATION: Using Percent Models

Work with a partner.

a. Find the missing values. What does the model represent?

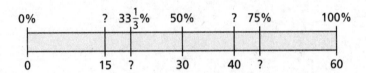

b. Label at least three percents and their corresponding numbers on the model below. How do you know you are correct?

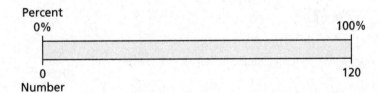

Name_____ Date _____

4.4 Solving Percent Problems (continued)

2 EXPLORATION: Solving a Percent Problem

Work with a partner. You purchase a national parks annual pass for 75% of the full price of the pass.

  a. Suppose you know the full price or the discounted price. How can you find the other price? Compare your answers with other students in your class.

  b. Suppose the full price of the pass is $80. How can you use a percent model to find the purchase price?

Percent
0%   100%

0
Dollars

4.4 Notetaking with Vocabulary

Vocabulary:

Notes:

4.4 Self-Assessment

Use the scale below to rate your understanding of the learning target and the success criteria.

1	2	3	4
I do not understand.	I can do it with help.	I can do it on my own.	I can teach someone else.

	Rating	Date
4.4 Solving Percent Problems		
Learning Target: Find a percent of a quantity and solve percent problems.	1 2 3 4	
I can represent percents of numbers using an equation, a ratio table, or a model.	1 2 3 4	
I can find percents of numbers.	1 2 3 4	
I can find the whole given a part and the percent.	1 2 3 4	

Name_____ Date _____

 Practice

Find the percent of the number. Explain your method.

1. 160% of 75   **2.** 230% of 45   **3.** 514% of 205   **4.** 115% of 130

Complete the statement using <, >, or =.

5. 55% of 60 ____ 60% of 65

6. 20% of 80 ____ 80% of 20

7. 36% of 150 ____ 27% of 200

8. 110% of 3 ____ 0.9% of 300

9. How many hours is 75% of 3 days?   **10.** How many feet is 20% of 4 miles?

11. A restaurant serves you a 16-fluid ounce glass of juice that is 30% ice. How many fluid ounces of juice do you actually get?

12. The table shows the grading scale for one of your classes.

Letter grade	A	B	C	D
Percent range	90-100%	80-89%	70-79%	60-69%

Tell the letter grade that you earn for each score.

a. You earn 14 out of a possible 20 points on a quiz.

b. You earn 66 out of a possible 80 points on a test.

c. You earn 216 out of a possible 250 point for a report.

13. A 15% discount saves you $5 off the price of an electronic game. How much do you save off the regular price if the discount is raised to 45%? Explain your reasoning.

14. Draw two different rectangles with perimeters that are each 80% of the perimeter of the rectangle shown. Show the length and width of each rectangle.

45 ft

75 ft

15. A monitor that regularly costs $100 is on sale for 15% off. The salesperson offers you 20% off the sale price. What percent of the original price is the salesperson's price?

Name_____ Date_____

Chapter Self-Assessment

Use the scale below to rate your understanding of the learning target and the success criteria.

1 I do not understand.　　**2** I can do it with help.　　**3** I can do it on my own.　　**4** I can teach someone else.

	Rating	Date
4.1 Percents and Fractions		
Learning Target: Write percents as fractions and fractions as percents.	1　2　3　4	
I can draw models to represent fractions and percents.	1　2　3　4	
I can write percents as fractions.	1　2　3　4	
I can write equivalent fractions with denominators of 100.	1　2　3　4	
I can write fractions as percents.	1　2　3　4	
4.2 Percents and Decimals		
Learning Target: Write percents as decimals and decimals as percents.	1　2　3　4	
I can draw models to represent decimals.	1　2　3　4	
I can explain why the decimal point moves when multiplying and dividing by 100.	1　2　3　4	
I can write percents as decimals.	1　2　3　4	
I can write decimals as percents.	1　2　3　4	
4.3 Comparing and Ordering Fractions, Decimals and Percents		
Learning Target: Compare and order fractions, decimals, and percents.	1　2　3　4	
I can rewrite a group of fractions, decimals, and percents using the same representation.	1　2　3　4	
I can explain how to compare fractions, decimals, and percents.	1　2　3　4	
I can order fractions, decimals, and percents from least to greatest.	1　2　3　4	

Name_____ Date _____

	Rating	Date
4.4 Solving Percent Problems		
Learning Target: Find a percent of a quantity and solve percent problems.	1 2 3 4	
I can represent percents of numbers using an equation, a ratio table, or a model.	1 2 3 4	
I can find percents of numbers.	1 2 3 4	
I can find the whole given a part and the percent.	1 2 3 4	

Chapter 5 Review & Refresh

Write a sentence interpreting the expression.

1. $2 \times (126 + 2566)$

2. $4 \times (6425 + 25)$

3. $(65 - 23) + 3$

4. $(65,000 - 5169) + 58$

5. $(890 \div 2) \div 2$

6. $(65 \times 6) \div 3$

7. Write a real-life problem representing the expression below.

$$3 \times (20 + 6)$$

Chapter 5 **Review & Refresh** (continued)

Simplify the expression.

8. $4 - 8 \div 2$

9. $2^2 \cdot 3 - 3$

10. $16 - 32 \div 2^3$

11. $3(4^2 - 9)$

12. $12 + 16 \div 4 \cdot 2$

13. $24 - 18 \div 3 + 2$

14. $20 + 12 - 2(7 - 4)$

15. $4(3^3 - 7) \div 10$

16. A group of 4 adults and 5 children is visiting an amusement park. Admission is $15 per adult and $9 per child. Find the total cost of admission for the group.

5.1 Algebraic Expressions
For use with Exploration 5.1

Learning Target: Evaluate algebraic expressions given values of their values.

Success Criteria:
- I can identify parts of an algebraic expression.
- I can evaluate algebraic expressions with one or more variables.
- I can evaluate algebraic expressions with one or more operations.

1 EXPLORATION: Evaluating Expressions

Work with a partner. Identify any missing information that is needed to answer each question. Then choose a reasonable quantity and write an expression for each problem. After you have written the expression, evaluate it using mental math or some other method.

a. You receive $24 for washing cars. How much do you earn per hour?

b. You buy 5 silicone baking molds at a craft store. How much do you spend?

5.1 **Algebraic Expressions** (continued)

c. You are running in a mud race. How much farther do you have to go after running 2000 feet?

d. A rattlesnake is 25 centimeters long when it hatches. The snake grows at a rate of about 1.6 centimeters per month for several months. What is the length of the rattlesnake?

5.1 Notetaking with Vocabulary

Vocabulary:

Notes:

5.1 Self-Assessment

Use the scale below to rate your understanding of the learning target and the success criteria.

1	**2**	**3**	**4**
I do not understand.	I can do it with help.	I can do it on my own.	I can teach someone else.

	Rating	Date
5.1 Algebraic Expressions		
Learning Target: Evaluate algebraic expressions given values of their variables.	1 2 3 4	
I can identify parts of an algebraic expression.	1 2 3 4	
I can evaluate algebraic expressions with one or more variables.	1 2 3 4	
I can evaluate algebraic expressions with one or more operations.	1 2 3 4	

5.1 Practice

Evaluate the expression when $d = 8$ and $e = 16$.

1. $4d + 3$

2. $48 \div d$

3. $\dfrac{2d}{e}$

4. Complete the table.

x	5	8	12
$9x - 5$			
$x^2 + 4$			
$2x^2 + 3x$			

5. On a field trip, your class stops to get ice cream cones. The cost is $3n$ dollars for n ice cream cones.

   a. There are 32 boys and 36 girls in your class. How much will the ice cream cones cost?

   b. One-fourth of the students want an ice cream sandwich rather than an ice cream cone. The expression $3n + 2m$ is the cost for n ice cream cones and m ice cream sandwiches. How much will the ice cream cones and ice cream sandwiches cost?

6. You and your friend each earn $(14h + 5c)$ dollars for washing h houses and c cars. Last month you washed 10 houses and your friend washed 28 cars. Who earned more money, *you*, *your friend*, or *neither*.

7. The expression $3p + 2f + s$ is the number of points earned by a basketball team for p three-point shots, f two-point field goals, and s one-point foul shots. Your opponents made 8 three-pointers, 12 two-point field goals, and 11 one-point foul shots. Your team made 10 three-pointers and 8 two-point field goals. What is the minimum number of one-point foul shots your team must make to win the game?

8. There are 46 legs in a zoo exhibit. Every animal has either two or four legs. The expression $2m + 4n$ is the total number of legs for m two-legged animals and n four-legged animals in the exhibit.

   a. List possible values for m and n so that the total number of legs is 46.

   b. The number of two-legged animals is 2 more than the number of four-legged animals. How many of each are in the exhibit?

   c. The number of legs in the exhibit increases by 4. What might account for this increase?

5.2 Writing Expressions
For use with Exploration 5.2

Learning Target: Write algebraic expressions and solve problems involving algebraic expressions.

Success Criteria:
- I can write numerical expressions.
- I can write algebraic expressions.
- I can write and evaluate algebraic expressions that represent real-life problems.

---

1 EXPLORATION: Writing Expressions

Work with a partner. You use a $20 bill to buy lunch at a café. You order a sandwich from the menu board shown.

CHEF RECOMMENDS
Sandwiches

Chicken Salad	Egg Salad	Grilled Cheese
$4.95	$4.65	$4.65
Reuben	Roast Beef	BLT
$6.45	$6.75	$5.25

Prices include tax.

a. Complete the table. In the last column, write a numerical expression for the amount of change you receive.

Sandwich	Price (dollars)	Change Received (dollars)
Reuben		
BLT		
Egg salad		
Roast beef		

5.2 **Writing Expressions** (continued)

b. Write an algebraic expression that represents the amount of change you receive when you order any sandwich from the menu board.

c. The expression $20 - 4.65s$ represents the amount of change one customer receives after ordering from the menu board. Explain what each part of the expression represents. Do you know what the customer ordered? Explain your reasoning.

Name_____ Date_____

5.2 Notetaking with Vocabulary

Vocabulary:

Notes:

5.2 Self-Assessment

Use the scale below to rate your understanding of the learning target and the success criteria.

1	**2**	**3**	**4**
I do not understand.	I can do it with help.	I can do it on my own.	I can teach someone else.

	Rating	Date
5.2 Writing Expressions		
Learning Target: Write algebraic expressions and solve problems involving algebraic expressions.	1 2 3 4	
I can write numerical expressions.	1 2 3 4	
I can write algebraic expressions.	1 2 3 4	
I can write and evaluate algebraic expressions that represent real-life problems.	1 2 3 4	

5.2 Practice

Write the phrase as an expression.

1. twice a number n plus 6

2. 7 less than 3 times a number m

3. the total of a number f and 3

4. the difference of a number w cubed and 25

5. You have two cats. Each cat has a litter of k kittens. Write an expression that describes the total number of cats and kittens you have.

6. The total of your dinner bill plus tip is $19.00. You left a $3.00 tip.

    a. The $3.00 tip is what percent of the dinner bill?

    b. The percent in part (a) is your customary tip percentage. Write an expression for the total of a dinner bill plus tip, for any d dinner bill.

Write the phrase as an expression. Then evaluate when $x = 8$ and $y = 20$.

7. fifteen more than the quotient of 24 and a number x

8. the sum of a number y and 30, all divided by 5

9. the product of 2 and the sum of a number x and 9

10. In the sequence, 2, 5, 8, 11, ..., x, ..., which expression describes the number after x? Explain your choice.

    A. $x + 3$ **B.** $x - 3$ **C.** $3x$ **D.** $x \div 3$

11. You are baking cookies.

    a. Each batch makes 24 cookies. You make x batches of cookies, but eat 5 cookies as you are baking. Write an expression for the number of cookies that you have.

    b. Is your answer to part (a) the same if you eat 5 cookies from each batch as you are baking? Explain your answer.

    c. You make 3 batches of cookies to make bags for a sale. You put 5 cookies in each bag. Given $14(5) + 2 = 3(24)$, what do the terms represent?

12. One number is one-third another. The lesser number is x. Write an expression that represents the greater number.

Name_____ Date_____

5.3 Properties of Addition and Multiplication
For use with Exploration 5.3

Learning Target: Identify equivalent expressions and apply properties to generate equivalent expressions.

Success Criteria:
- I can explain the meaning of equivalent expressions.
- I can use properties of addition to generate equivalent expressions.
- I can use properties of multiplication to generate equivalent expressions.

1 EXPLORATION: Identifying Equivalent Expressions

Work with a partner.

a. Choose four values for a variable x. Then evaluate each expression for each value of x. Are any of the expressions *equivalent*? Explain your reasoning.

x				
4 + x + 4				

x				
16x				

x				
4 • (x • 4)				

x				
x + 4 + 4				

x				
x + 8				

x				
(4 • x) • 4				

5.3 **Properties of Addition and Multiplication** (continued)

b. You have used the following properties in a previous course. Use the examples to explain the meaning of each property.

> **Commutative Property of Addition:** $3 + 5 = 5 + 3$

> **Commutative Property of Multiplication:** $9 \cdot 3 = 3 \cdot 9$

> **Associative Property of Addition:** $8 + (3 + 1) = (8 + 3) + 1$

> **Associative Property of Multiplication:** $12 \cdot (6 \cdot 2) = (12 \cdot 6) \cdot 2$

Are these properties true for algebraic expressions? Explain your reasoning.

5.3 Notetaking with Vocabulary

Vocabulary:

Notes:

5.3 Self-Assessment

Use the scale below to rate your understanding of the learning target and the success criteria.

1	2	3	4
I do not understand.	I can do it with help.	I can do it on my own.	I can teach someone else.

	Rating	Date
5.3 Properties of Addition and Multiplication		
Learning Target: Identify equivalent expressions and apply properties to generate equivalent expressions.	1 2 3 4	
I can explain the meaning of equivalent expressions.	1 2 3 4	
I can use properties of addition to generate equivalent expressions.	1 2 3 4	
I can use properties of multiplication to generate equivalent expressions.	1 2 3 4	

5.3 Practice

Complete the statement using the specified property.

1. Commutative Property of Addition: $h + 11 =$ ____

2. Commutative Property of Multiplication: $12 \cdot k =$ ____

3. Associative Property of Addition: $21 + (9 + 8) =$ ____

4. Associative Property of Multiplication: $12 \cdot (5 \cdot 4) =$ ____

5. Multiplication Property of One: $18 \cdot w \cdot 1 =$ ____

6. Addition Property of Zero: $26 + c + 0 =$ ____

7. Describe and correct the error made in identifying the property.

$$\times \quad (2 \cdot x) \cdot 4 = 2 \cdot (x \cdot 4)$$
Commutative Property of Multiplication

8. On a bike trip, you traveled 21 miles on the first day, and n miles on the second day. On the 3rd day, you traveled 5 miles less than on the second day.

   a. Write an expression for the number of miles traveled in three days.

   b. Simplify the expression. Explain each step.

   c. Find the number of miles traveled in three days when you traveled 19 miles on the second day.

9. You and 13 friends play on a softball team. A sponsor paid for the league fee, each player's T-shirt, new bats for the team, and 2 new softballs for each game of the season. An expression that represents the total amount (in dollars) paid by the sponsor is $14x + 20(2y) + 5z + 120$.

   a. Which addend represents the league fee? Explain your reasoning.

   b. Which addend represents the T-shirts? Explain your reasoning.

   c. What does y represent?

Name_____ Date _____

 5.4 **The Distributive Property**
For use with Exploration 5.4

Learning Target: Apply the Distributive Property to generate equivalent expressions.

Success Criteria:
- I can explain how to apply the Distributive Property.
- I can use the Distributive Property to simplify algebraic expressions.
- I can use the Distributive Property to combine like terms.

1 **EXPLORATION:** Using Models to Simplify Expressions

Work with a partner.

a. Use the models to simplify the expressions. Explain your reasoning.

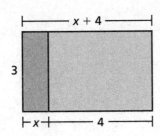

$3(x + 4) = \boxed{}$

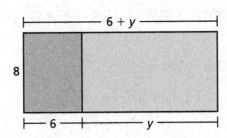

$8(6 + y) = \boxed{}$

$5n + 4n = \boxed{}$

$5n - 4n = \boxed{}$

5.4 The Distributive Property (continued)

b. In part (a), check that the original expressions are equivalent to the simplified expressions.

c. You used the Distributive Property in a previous course. Use the example to explain the meaning of the property.

Distributive Property: $6(20 + 3) = 6(20) + 6(3)$

Is this property true for algebraic expressions? Explain your reasoning.

Name_____ Date _____

5.4 Notetaking with Vocabulary

Vocabulary:

Notes:

5.4 Self-Assessment

Use the scale below to rate your understanding of the learning target and the success criteria.

1	**2**	**3**	**4**
I do not understand.	I can do it with help.	I can do it on my own.	I can teach someone else.

	Rating	Date
5.4 The Distributive Property		
Learning Target: Apply the Distributive Property to generate equivalent expressions.	1 2 3 4	
I can explain how to apply the Distributive Property.	1 2 3 4	
I can use the Distributive Property to simplify algebraic expressions.	1 2 3 4	
I can use the Distributive Property to combine like terms.	1 2 3 4	

5.4 Practice

Match the expression with an equivalent expression.

1. $10(m-3)$ 2. $2(5m-3)$ 3. $2(5m-10)$ 4. $10(m-10)$

     A. $10m-6$ **B.** $5(2m-20)$ **C.** $5(2m-4)$ **D.** $10m-30$

5. Describe and correct the error in rewriting the expression.

$$\boxed{\quad \times \quad 6(x+7) = 6x + 13 \quad}$$

6. You are y years old. Your sister is 3 years older than you. Your uncle is 4 times older than your sister. Write and simplify an expression that represents your uncle's age.

Simplify the expression.

7. $4(y+11)-10$ 8. $3.2(d+1.7)$ 9. $\frac{2}{3}\left(x-\frac{5}{6}\right)+4x$

Evaluate each product by (1) rewriting the mixed number as a sum and using the Distributive Property and (2) rewriting the mixed number as an improper fraction and multiplying fractions. Which method do you prefer? Is your preference the same for all three expressions? Explain your reasoning.

10. $\frac{3}{7} \times 5\frac{1}{2}$ 11. $\frac{5}{12} \times 4\frac{3}{10}$ 12. $\frac{3}{8} \times 3\frac{1}{6}$

Find the value of x that makes the expressions equivalent.

13. $3(x-7);\ 33-21$ 14. $5(x+4);\ 15+20$

15. Add one set of parentheses to the expression $8 \cdot x + 10 + 2x + 4 \cdot x + 8 - 6$ so that it is equivalent to $2(7x + 18)$.

16. Your locker contains x textbooks, 3 more notebooks than textbooks, twice as many pencils as notebooks, and 2.5 times as many candy bars as pencils. Write and simplify an expression that represents the number of candy bars in your locker.

Name_____ Date_____

5.5 Factoring Expressions
For use with Exploration 5.5

Learning Target: Factor numerical and algebraic expressions.

Success Criteria:
- I can use the Distributive Property to factor numerical expressions.
- I can identify the greatest common factor of terms including variables.
- I can use the Distributive Property to factor algebraic expressions.
- I can interpret factored expressions in real-life problems.

 EXPLORATION: Finding Dimensions

Work with a partner.

a. The models show the area (in square units) of each part of a rectangle. Use the models to find missing values that complete the expressions. Explain your reasoning.

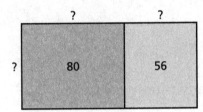

$$8 + 24 = \boxed{}\left(\boxed{} + \boxed{}\right)$$

$$80 + 56 = \boxed{}\left(\boxed{} + \boxed{}\right)$$

5.5 **Factoring Expressions** (continued)

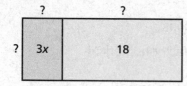

$$3x + 18 = \boxed{} \left(\boxed{} + \boxed{} \right)$$

b. In part (a), check that the original expressions are equivalent to the expressions you wrote. Explain your reasoning.

c. Explain how you can use the Distributive Property to rewrite a sum of two whole numbers with a common factor.

Notetaking with Vocabulary

Vocabulary:

Notes:

 Self-Assessment

Use the scale below to rate your understanding of the learning target and the success criteria.

1	2	3	4
I do not understand.	I can do it with help.	I can do it on my own.	I can teach someone else.

	Rating	Date
5.5 Factoring Expressions		
Learning Target: Factor numerical and algebraic expressions.	1 2 3 4	
I can use the Distributive Property to factor numerical expressions.	1 2 3 4	
I can identify the greatest common factor of terms including variables.	1 2 3 4	
I can use the Distributive Property to factor algebraic expressions.	1 2 3 4	
I can interpret factored expressions in real-life problems.	1 2 3 4	

Name _____ Date _____

1. Which expression is not equivalent to $12x - 18$?

   A. $6(2x - 3)$ **B.** $2(6x - 9)$ **C.** $9(3x - 2)$ **D.** $3(4x - 6)$

Factor the expression using the GCF.

2. $18x + 6$ 3. $27x - 18y$ 4. $42x + 28y$

5. Use the Distributive Property to write five expressions that are equivalent to $20x + 100$.

6. The length of a rectangle is 6 centimeters and its area is $(6x + 18)$ square centimeters. Write an expression for the width.

7. The expression $24x + 12$ is factored as $a(bx + c)$.

   a. Write all the possible whole number values of a.

   b. Write all the possible whole number values of c.

8. You purchase 4 videos. The original price of each video is x dollars. You decide to purchase the Limited Edition versions of the videos for an additional cost. Your total cost is $(4x + 20)$ dollars. What can you conclude about the additional cost of the Limited Edition version of a video?

9. Your friend factors the expression $48x - 16$. Is your friend correct? Explain your reasoning.

   $$\begin{aligned} 48x - 16 &= 16(3x) - 16 \\ &= 16(3x) \\ &= 48x \end{aligned}$$

10. You sell coffee mugs for a fund raiser. For each coffee mug you sell, the company that makes the mug receives x dollars, and you receive the remaining amount. You sell m mugs for a total of $(mx + mk)$ dollars.

    a. What does the expression mx represent?

    b. What does mk represent?

    c. Use the Distributive Property to write an equivalent expression to $mx + mk$.

    d. How much money do you receive for each coffee mug that you sell?

Name_____ Date _____

Chapter 5 Chapter Self-Assessment

Use the scale below to rate your understanding of the learning target and the success criteria.

1	**2**	**3**	**4**
I do not understand.	I can do it with help.	I can do it on my own.	I can teach someone else.

	Rating	Date
5.1 Algebraic Expressions		
Learning Target: Evaluate algebraic expressions given values of their variables.	1 2 3 4	
I can identify parts of an algebraic expression.	1 2 3 4	
I can evaluate algebraic expressions with one or more variables.	1 2 3 4	
I can evaluate algebraic expressions with one or more operations.	1 2 3 4	
5.2 Writing Expressions		
Learning Target: Write algebraic expressions and solve problems involving algebraic expressions.	1 2 3 4	
I can write numerical expressions.	1 2 3 4	
I can write algebraic expressions.	1 2 3 4	
I can write and evaluate algebraic expressions that represent real-life problems.	1 2 3 4	
5.3 Properties of Addition and Multiplication		
Learning Target: Identify equivalent expressions and apply properties to generate equivalent expressions.	1 2 3 4	
I can explain the meaning of equivalent expressions.	1 2 3 4	
I can use properties of addition to generate equivalent expressions.	1 2 3 4	
I can use properties of multiplication to generate equivalent expressions.	1 2 3 4	

	Rating	Date
5.4 The Distributive Property		
Learning Target: Apply the Distributive Property to generate equivalent expressions.	1 2 3 4	
I can explain how to apply the Distributive Property.	1 2 3 4	
I can use the Distributive Property to simplify algebraic expressions.	1 2 3 4	
I can use the Distributive Property to combine like terms.	1 2 3 4	
5.5 Factoring Expressions		
Learning Target: Factor numerical and algebraic expressions.	1 2 3 4	
I can use the Distributive Property to factor numerical expressions.	1 2 3 4	
I can identify the greatest common factor of terms including variables.	1 2 3 4	
I can use the Distributive Property to factor algebraic expressions.	1 2 3 4	
I can interpret factored expressions in real-life problems.	1 2 3 4	

Chapter 6 Review & Refresh

Evaluate the expression when $x = 3$ and $y = 5$.

1. $2xy$

2. $\dfrac{6y}{x}$

3. $4y - x$

4. $y^2 - 7x + 2$

Evaluate the expression when $x = \frac{1}{4}$ and $y = 8$.

5. $3xy$

6. $16x + 5y$

7. $\dfrac{y}{2x}$

8. $2(10 - 24x) + y^2$

9. After m months, you paid $25 + 10m$ for your computer. How much did you pay after 6 months?

Chapter 6 Review & Refresh (continued)

Write the phrase as an expression.

10. three more than twice a number k

11. half of a number q plus eight

12. a number p decreased by six

13. nine times a number x

14. five divided by a number n

15. one plus the product of a number y and three

16. Each classmate contributes $2 for charity. Write an expression for the amount of money raised by your class.

17. You save half of the money from your paycheck plus an extra six dollars to buy a new bike. Write an expression for the amount of money you save from each paycheck.

Writing Equations in One Variable
For use with Exploration 6.1

Learning Target: Write equations in one variable and write equations that represent real-life problems.

Success Criteria:
- I can identify key words and phrases that indicate equality.
- I can write word sentences as equations.
- I can create equations to represent real-life problems.

1 **EXPLORATION:** Writing Equations

Work with a partner.
Customers order sandwiches at a café from the menu board shown.

a. The equation $6.75x = 20.25$ represents the purchase of one customer from the menu board. What does the equation tell you about the purchase? What cannot be determined from the equation?

6.1 **Writing Equations in One Variable** (continued)

b. The four customers in the table buy multiple sandwiches of the same type. For each customer, write an equation that represents the situation. Then determine how many sandwiches each customer buys. Explain your reasoning.

	Sandwich	Amount Used For Payment	Change Received
Customer A	Reuben	$20	$0.65
Customer B	Chicken salad	$10	$0.10
Customer C	BLT	$30	$9.00
Customer D	Egg salad	$50	$26.75

Notetaking with Vocabulary

Vocabulary:

Notes:

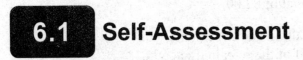

Self-Assessment

Use the scale below to rate your understanding of the learning target and
the success criteria.

1	2	3	4
I do not understand.	I can do it with help.	I can do it on my own.	I can teach someone else.

	Rating	Date
6.1 Writing Equations in One Variable		
Learning Target: Write equations in one variable and write equations that represent real-life problems.	1 2 3 4	
I can identify key words and phrases that indicate equality.	1 2 3 4	
I can write word sentences as equations.	1 2 3 4	
I can create equations to represent real-life problems.	1 2 3 4	

Name_____ Date _____

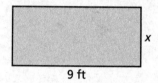

6.1 Practice

Write the word sentence as an equation.

1. $7\frac{2}{3}$ is the product of a number x and $2\frac{1}{8}$.

2. 12.4 increased by a number k equals 19.

Write an equation you can use to find the value of x.

3. Area of rectangle: 36 ft

4. Area of triangle: 108 cm^2

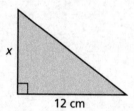

9 ft

12 cm

5. You want to put 520 quarters in coin wrappers. You need one wrapper for every \$10 in quarters. Write an equation you can use to find how many wrappers w you need.

6. You use a metal detector at the beach. You find 2 quarters, 12 dimes, and 23 pennies. Write an equation you can use to find how many more pennies p you need to find in order to have a total of \$2.00.

7. In one minute, you climb halfway up a rock wall. In another minute, you are 24 feet above the ground after covering half of the remaining height. Write an equation you can use to find the total height h of the rock wall.

8. A golf driving range has small buckets of golf balls for \$6 each and medium buckets of golf balls for \$8 each. One day, golfers use 27 small buckets and some medium buckets for a total cost of \$626. Write an equation you can use to find the number m of medium buckets used.

9. A silkworm winds its cocoon out of one long silk fiber. To make silk thread, 3 to 10 of these silk fibers are unwound from their cocoons and combined into a single thread with a typical length of 300 yards.

   a. Explain why you cannot write an equation to find the exact total length of the silk fibers used in a 300-yard silk thread.

   b. Choose a reasonable number of silk fibers in a thread. Write an equation to find the total length of the silk fibers used in 300 yards of the thread.

Name_____ Date_____

6.2 Solving Equations Using Addition or Subtraction
For use with Exploration 6.2

Learning Target: Write and solve equations using addition or subtraction.

Success Criteria:
- I can determine whether a value is a solution of an equation.
- I can apply the Addition and Subtraction Properties of Equality to generate equivalent equations.
- I can solve equations using addition or subtraction.
- I can create equations involving addition or subtraction to solve real-life problems.

---

1 EXPLORATION: Solving an Equation Using a Tape Diagram

Work with a partner. A student solves an equation using the tape diagram below.

Step 1:
12

x	4

Step 2:
8	4

x	4

Step 3:
8

x

a. What equation did the student solve? What is the solution?

b. Explain how the tape diagrams in Steps 2 and 3 relate to the equation and its solution.

6.2 **Solving Equations Using Addition or Subtraction** (continued)

---

2 **EXPLORATION:** Solving an Equation Using a Model

Work with a partner.

When two sides of a scale weigh the same, the scale will balance.

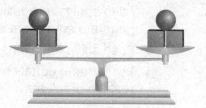

a. How are the two sides of an equation similar to a balanced scale?

b. When you add weight to one side of a balanced scale, what can you do to balance the scale? What if you subtract weight from one side of a balanced scale? How does this relate to solving an equation?

c. Use a model to solve $x + 2 = 7$. Describe how you can solve the equation algebraically.

Name_____ Date_____

6.2 Notetaking with Vocabulary

Vocabulary:

Notes:

6.2 Self-Assessment

Use the scale below to rate your understanding of the learning target and
the success criteria.

1	2	3	4
I do not understand.	I can do it with help.	I can do it on my own.	I can teach someone else.

	Rating	Date
6.2 Solving Equations Using Addition or Subtraction		
Learning Target: Write and solve equations using addition or subtraction.	1 2 3 4	
I can determine whether a value is a solution of an equation.	1 2 3 4	
I can apply the Addition and Subtraction Properties of Equality to generate equivalent equations.	1 2 3 4	
I can solve equations using addition or subtraction.	1 2 3 4	
I can create equations involving addition or subtraction to solve real-life problems.	1 2 3 4	

6.2 Practice

Write the word sentence as an equation. Then solve the equation.

1. 27 less than a number *h* equals 3.5.

2. The sum of a number *b* and 4.7 equals 10.9.

Write and solve an addition equation to find *x*.

3. Perimeter = 30 in.

4. Perimeter = 43 m

5. Perimeter = 16 ft

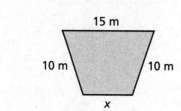

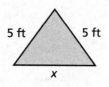

6. You are grocery shopping.

   a. Write and solve three equations to find the cost *m* of the milk, the cost *c* of the cereal, and the cost *e* of the eggs.

   b. You have *d* dollars. You purchase one of each item and you have $0.08 left. Write and solve an equation to find your original amount of money *d*.

   Grocery Items

   Bread: $2.19
   Milk: $1.56 more than bread
   Cereal: $3.20 more than eggs
   Eggs: $2.36 less than milk

7. A jacket is on sale for $10 off. You have a coupon worth $5.80 that brings the cost of the jacket down to $33.19. Write and solve an equation to find the original cost *c* of the jacket.

8. You have $71. You earn some money washing your Mom's car to help you buy the new video game that costs $78.75. After you buy the game, you have $7.25 left. Write and solve an equation to find how much money you earned washing Mom's car.

9. Just by looking at the equation $2(x - 3) + 7 = 2(x - 3) + x$, find the value of *x*. Explain your reasoning.

10. Consider the equation $9 - x = 5$.

    a. Solve the equation by first adding *x* to both sides.

    b. Solve the equation by first subtracting 9 from both sides.

    c. Which approach, (a) or (b), did you prefer? Explain.

6.3 Solving Equations Using Multiplication or Division
For use with Exploration 6.3

Learning Target: Write and solve equations using multiplication or division.

Success Criteria:
- I can apply the Multiplication and Division Properties of Equality to generate equivalent equations.
- I can solve equations using multiplication or division.
- I can create equations involving multiplication or division to solve real-life problems.

1 EXPLORATION: Solving an Equation Using a Tape Diagram

Work with a partner. A student solves an equation using the tape diagrams below.

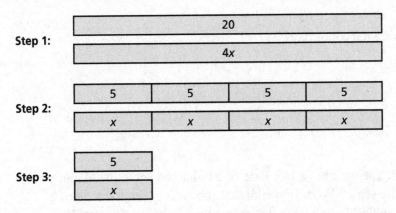

a. What equation did the student solve? What is the solution?

b. Explain how the tape diagrams in Steps 2 and 3 relate to the equation and its solution.

6.3 Solving Equations Using Multiplication or Division (continued)

2 **EXPLORATION:** Solving an Equation Using a Model

Work with a partner. Three robots go out to
lunch. They decide to split the $12 bill evenly.
The scale represents the number of robots and
the price of the meal.

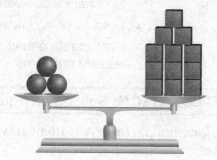

a. How much does each robot pay?

b. When you triple the weight on one side of a balanced scale, what can you
do to balance the scale? What if you divide the weight on one side of a
balanced scale in half? How does this relate to solving an equation?

c. Use a model to solve $5x = 15$. Describe how you can solve the equation
algebraically.

6.3 Notetaking with Vocabulary

Vocabulary:

Notes:

6.3 Self-Assessment

Use the scale below to rate your understanding of the learning target and the success criteria.

1	2	3	4
I do not understand.	I can do it with help.	I can do it on my own.	I can teach someone else.

	Rating	Date
6.3 Solving Equations Using Multiplication or Division		
Learning Target: Write and solve equations using multiplication or division.	1 2 3 4	
I can apply the Multiplication and Division Properties of Equality to generate equivalent equations.	1 2 3 4	
I can solve equations using multiplication or division.	1 2 3 4	
I can create equations involving multiplication or division to solve real-life problems.	1 2 3 4	

6.3 Practice

Solve the equation. Check your solution.

1. $\dfrac{4v}{27} = 16$

2. $13 \cdot x = 84.5$

3. $\dfrac{3c}{8.1} = 22.8$

Solve for x. Check your answer.

4. Rectangle

Area = 84 square units

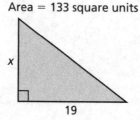

12

5. Triangle

Area = 133 square units

x

19

6. Show how you can solve the equation $\dfrac{1}{5}x = 4$ by dividing each side by $\dfrac{1}{5}$.

7. You want to know the side length of the square swimming pool. Explain how you can use the perimeter. Then find the side length to the nearest yard.

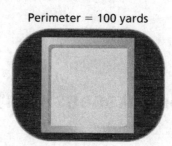

Perimeter = 100 yards

8. Your family has a car with a 15-gallon gas tank. Find the price of one gallon of gas in your area. Then write and solve a division equation to find the price p to fill the car's gas tank when it is empty.

9. Using a special discount, you download 15 songs for $10.68. The regular price of each song is $0.89. What is the percent of the discount?

10. You buy dog biscuits at the bulk rate price of $2.25 per pound. The scale shows the weight of 25 biscuits. Find the cost of 40 biscuits. Explain how you found your answer.

6.4 Writing Equations in Two Variables
For use with Exploration 6.4

Learning Target: Write equations in two variables and analyze the relationship between the two quantities.

Success Criteria:
- I can determine whether an ordered pair is a solution of an equation in two variables.
- I can distinguish between independent and dependent variables.
- I can write and graph an equation in two variables.
- I can create equations in two variables to solve real-life problems.

---

1 EXPLORATION: Writing Equations in Two Variables

Work with a partner. In Section 3.4 Exploration 1, you used a ratio table to create a graph for an airplane traveling 300 miles per hour. Below is one possible ratio table and graph.

Time (hours)	1	2	3	4
Distance (miles)	300	600	900	1200

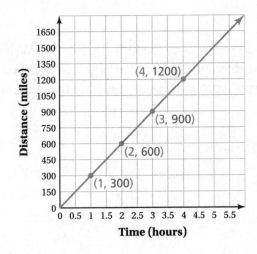

a. Describe the relationship between the two quantities. Which quantity *depends* on the other quantity?

6.4 **Writing Equations in Two Variables** (continued)

b. Use variables to write an equation that represents the relationship between the time and the distance. What can you do with this equation? Provide an example.

c. Suppose the airplane is 1500 miles away from its destination. Write an equation that represents the relationship between time and distance from the destination. How can you represent this relationship using a graph?

6.4 Notetaking with Vocabulary

Vocabulary:

Notes:

6.4 Self-Assessment

Use the scale below to rate your understanding of the learning target and the success criteria.

1	2	3	4
I do not understand.	I can do it with help.	I can do it on my own.	I can teach someone else.

	Rating	Date
6.4 Writing Equations in Two Variables		
Learning Target: Write equations in two variables and analyze the relationship between the two quantities.	1 2 3 4	
I can determine whether an ordered pair is a solution of an equation in two variables.	1 2 3 4	
I can distinguish between independent and dependent variables.	1 2 3 4	
I can write and graph an equation in two variables.	1 2 3 4	
I can create equations in two variables to solve real-life problems.	1 2 3 4	

Name_____ Date _____

Write a formula for the given measure. Tell what each variable represents. Identify the independent and dependent variables.

1. The perimeter of a rectangle with a length of 8 feet

2. The area of a rectangle with a width of 2 centimeters

3. Describe and correct the error in finding a solution of the equation in two variables.

> ✗ $y = 5x - 4$; (2, 6)
> $2 = 5(2) - 4$
> $2 = 6$
> (2, 6) is not a solution.

Complete the table by describing possible independent or dependent variables.

4.

Independent Variable	Dependent Variable
The number of lawns you mow	

5.

Independent Variable	Dependent Variable
	The number of shopping bags

6. Your video membership costs $14 per month for 10 video rentals. Each additional video rental is $2.

   a. Write an equation in two variables that represents the monthly cost of your video rentals.

   b. Identify the independent and dependent variables.

7. Write an equation that has (2, -3) as a solution.

Name_____ Date_____

Chapter Self-Assessment

Use the scale below to rate your understanding of the learning target and the success criteria.

1	2	3	4
I do not understand.	I can do it with help.	I can do it on my own.	I can teach someone else.

	Rating	Date
6.1 Writing Equations in One Variable		
Learning Target: Write equations in one variable and write equations that represent real-life problems.	1 2 3 4	
I can identify key words and phrases that indicate equality.	1 2 3 4	
I can write word sentences as equations.	1 2 3 4	
I can create equations to represent real-life problems.	1 2 3 4	
6.2 Solving Equations Using Addition or Subtraction		
Learning Target: Write and solve equations using addition or subtraction.	1 2 3 4	
I can determine whether a value is a solution of an equation.	1 2 3 4	
I can apply the Addition and Subtraction Properties of Equality to generate equivalent equations.	1 2 3 4	
I can solve equations using addition or subtraction.	1 2 3 4	
I can create equations involving addition or subtraction to solve real-life problems.	1 2 3 4	
6.3 Solving Equations Using Multiplication or Division		
Learning Target: Write and solve equations using multiplication or division.	1 2 3 4	
I can apply the Multiplication and Division Properties of Equality to generate equivalent equations.	1 2 3 4	
I can solve equations using multiplication or division.	1 2 3 4	
I can create equations involving multiplication or division to solve real-life problems.	1 2 3 4	

Chapter Self-Assessment (continued)

	Rating	Date
6.4 Writing Equations in Two Variables		
Learning Target: Write equations in two variables and analyze the relationship between the two quantities.	1 2 3 4	
I can determine whether an ordered pair is a solution of an equation in two variables.	1 2 3 4	
I can distinguish between independent and dependent variables.	1 2 3 4	
I can write and graph an equation in two variables.	1 2 3 4	
I can create equations in two variables to solve real-life problems.	1 2 3 4	

Name_____ Date_____

Identify the figure.

1.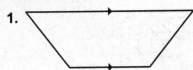

2.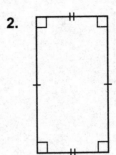

3.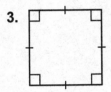

4.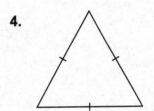

5. Identify the figure.

6 in.

6 in.   6 in.

6 in.

Chapter 7 **Review & Refresh** (continued)

Find the volume of the rectangular prism.

6.

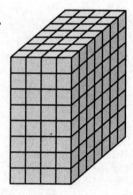

7.

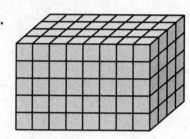

8.

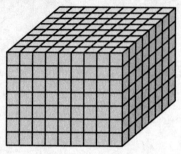

9.

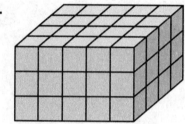

10.

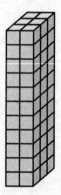

11.

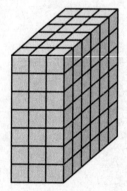

7.1 Areas of Parallelograms
For use with Exploration 7.1

Learning Target: Find areas and missing dimensions of parallelograms.

Success Criteria:
- I can explain how the area of a rectangle is used to find the area of a parallelogram.
- I can use the base and the height of a parallelogram to find its area.
- I can use the area of a parallelogram and one of its dimensions to find the other dimension.

---

1 EXPLORATION: Deriving the Area Formula of a Parallelogram

Work with a partner.

a. Draw *any* rectangle on a piece of centimeter grid paper. Cut the rectangle into two pieces that can be arranged to form a parallelogram. What do you notice about the areas of the rectangle and the parallelogram?

7.1 **Areas of Parallelograms** (continued)

b. Cut the parallelogram and rearrange the pieces to find its area.

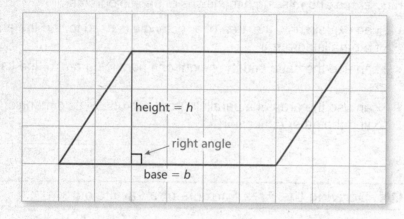

c. Draw *any* parallelogram on a piece of centimeter grid paper and find its area. Does the area change when you use a different side as the base? Explain your reasoning.

d. Use your results to write a formula for the area *A* of a parallelogram.

Name_____ Date_____

7.1 Notetaking with Vocabulary

Vocabulary:

Notes:

7.1 Self-Assessment

Use the scale below to rate your understanding of the learning target and the success criteria.

1	**2**	**3**	**4**
I do not understand.	I can do it with help.	I can do it on my own.	I can teach someone else.

	Rating	Date
7.1 Areas of Parallelograms		
Learning Target: Find areas and missing dimensions of parallelograms.	1 2 3 4	
I can explain how the area of a rectangle is used to find the area of a parallelogram.	1 2 3 4	
I can use the base and the height of a parallelogram to find its area.	1 2 3 4	
I can use the area of a parallelogram and one of its dimensions to find the other dimension.	1 2 3 4	

7.1 Practice

1. A billboard is in the shape of a parallelogram. The billboard has a base of 48 feet and a height of 14 feet. Find the area of the billboard.

Find the area of the shaded region.

2.

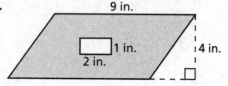

3.

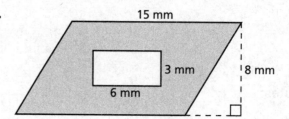

4. The mosaic tile design consists of one square and four parallelograms. Find the area of the design.

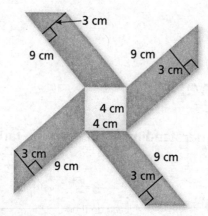

5. Your parallelogram has a base of 17 centimeters and a height of 12 centimeters. Your friend's parallelogram also has a base of 17 centimeters.

   a. The area of your friend's parallelogram is 60% of the area of your parallelogram. What is the height of your friend's parallelogram?

   b. The height of your friend's parallelogram is what percent of the height of your parallelogram?

   c. Does this relationship hold if the height is the same rather than the base? Give an example.

7.2   # Areas of Triangles
For use with Exploration 7.2

Learning Target: Find areas and missing dimensions of triangles, and find areas of composite figures.

Success Criteria: • I can explain how the area of a parallelogram is used to find the area of a triangle.
   • I can use the base and the height of a triangle to find its area.
   • I can use the area of a triangle and one of its dimensions to find the other dimension.
   • I can use decomposition to find the area of a figure.

1 **EXPLORATION: Deriving the Area Formula of a Triangle**

Work with a partner.

a. Draw *any* parallelogram on a piece of centimeter grid paper. Cut the parallelogram into two identical triangles. How can you use the area of the parallelogram to find the area of each triangle?

b. Find the area of the triangle. Explain how you found the area.

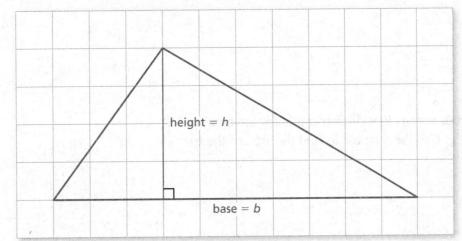

7.2 **Areas of Triangles** (continued)

c. Draw *any* acute triangle on a piece of centimeter grid paper and find its area. Repeat this process for a right triangle and an obtuse triangle.

d. Do the areas change in part (c) when you use different sides as the base? Explain your reasoning.

e. Use your results to write a formula for the area *A* of a triangle. Use the formula to find the area of the triangle shown.

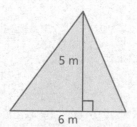

5 m

6 m

Name_____ Date_____

7.2 Notetaking with Vocabulary

Vocabulary:

Notes:

7.2 Self-Assessment

Use the scale below to rate your understanding of the learning target and the success criteria.

1	2	3	4
I do not understand.	I can do it with help.	I can do it on my own.	I can teach someone else.

	Rating	Date
7.2 Areas of Triangles		
Learning Target: Find areas and missing dimensions of triangles, and find areas of composite figures.	1 2 3 4	
I can explain how the area of a parallelogram is used to find the area of a triangle.	1 2 3 4	
I can use the base and the height of a triangle to find its area.	1 2 3 4	
I can use the area of a triangle and one of its dimensions to find the other dimension.	1 2 3 4	
I can use decomposition to find the area of a figure.	1 2 3 4	

Name_____ Date _____

7.2 Practice

1. A sign is in the shape of a triangle with a base of 12 inches and a height of 8 inches. Find the area of the sign.

Find the area of the figure.

2.
18 cm

7 cm

7 cm

18 cm

3.
17 ft

25 ft   21 ft

21 ft

4. The shaded triangle in the sign has a base of 750 millimeters and a height of 650 millimeters. The white triangle in the sign has a base of 375 millimeters and a height of 325 millimeters. Find the area of the shaded portion of the sign.

5. You live on a triangular piece of land with a base of 121 yards and a height of 80 yards. One acre of land is equal to 4840 square yards. Find the area of your piece of land in acres.

6. Triangle A and Triangle B have the same base.

   a. The height of Triangle B is twice the height of Triangle A. How many times greater is the area of Triangle B?

   b. The height of Triangle B is 3 times the height of Triangle A. How many times greater is the area of Triangle B?

   c. The height of Triangle B is one-half the height of Triangle A. How many times greater is the area of Triangle B?

   d. The height of Triangle B is n times the height of Triangle A. How many times greater is the area of Triangle B?

   e. Triangle A and Triangle B both have a base of 16 meters. Triangle A has a height of 9 meters. The height of Triangle B is 5 times the height of Triangle A. Does the relationship between the areas of Triangle A and Triangle B agree with part (d)? Explain.

7.3 Areas of Trapezoids and Kites
For use with Exploration 7.3

Learning Target: Find areas of trapezoids, kites, and composite figures.

Success Criteria: • I can explain how the area of a parallelogram is used to find the area of a trapezoid.
• I can decompose trapezoids and kites into smaller shapes.
• I can use decomposition to find the area of a figure.
• I can use the bases and the height of a trapezoid to find its area.

---

1   EXPLORATION: Deriving the Area Formula of a Trapezoid

Work with a partner.

a. Draw *any* parallelogram on a piece of centimeter grid paper. Cut the parallelogram into two identical trapezoids. How can you use the area of the parallelogram to find the area of each trapezoid?

b. Find the area of the trapezoid. Explain how you found the area.

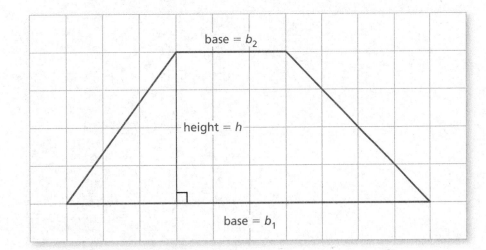

7.3 **Areas of Trapezoids and Kites** (continued)

c. Draw *any* trapezoid on a piece of centimeter grid paper and find its area.

d. Use your results to write a formula for the area *A* of a trapezoid. Use the formula to find the area of the trapezoid shown.

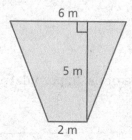

6 m

5 m

2 m

7.3 Notetaking with Vocabulary

Vocabulary:

Notes:

7.3 Self-Assessment

Use the scale below to rate your understanding of the learning target and the success criteria.

1	2	3	4
I do not understand.	I can do it with help.	I can do it on my own.	I can teach someone else.

	Rating	Date
7.3 Areas of Trapezoids and Kites		
Learning Target: Find areas of trapezoids, kites, and composite figures.	1 2 3 4	
I can explain how the area of a parallelogram is used to find the area of a trapezoid.	1 2 3 4	
I can decompose trapezoids and kites into smaller shapes.	1 2 3 4	
I can use decomposition to find the area of a figure.	1 2 3 4	
I can use the bases and the height of a trapezoid to find its area.	1 2 3 4	

7.3 Practice

1. The trapezoid consists of a triangle and a parallelogram. The area of the trapezoid is 48 square feet. Find the length of the base of the triangle.

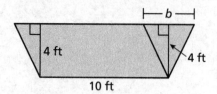

2. The area of the trapezoid is 40 square millimeters.

   a. Find two possible values for each base length.

   b. Is it possible for b_2 to equal 9 millimeters? Explain.

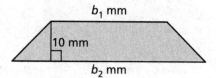

Find the area of the shaded figure.

3.

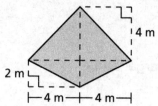

4.

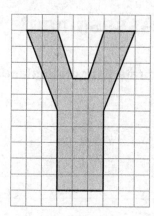

5.

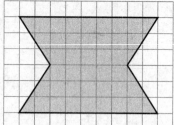

6.

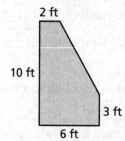

7.4 **Three-Dimensional Figures**
For use with Exploration 7.4

Learning Target: Describe and draw three-dimensional figures.

Success Criteria:
- I can find the numbers of faces, edges, and vertices of a three-dimensional figure.
- I can draw prisms and pyramids.
- I can draw the front, side, and top views of a three-dimensional figure.

---

1 EXPLORATION: Exploring Faces, Edges, and Vertices

Work with a partner. Use the rectangular prism shown.

a. Prisms have *faces*, *edges*, and *vertices*. What does each of these terms mean?

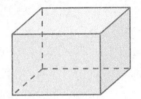

b. What does it mean for lines or planes to be parallel or perpendicular in three dimensions? Use drawings to identify one pair of each of the following.

parallel faces   perpendicular faces

parallel edges   perpendicular edges

edge parallel to a face   edge perpendicular to a face

7.4 **Three-Dimensional Figures** (continued)

---

2 **EXPLORATION:** Drawing Views of a Solid

Work with a partner. Draw the front, side, and top views of each stack of cubes. Then find the number of cubes in the stack. An example is shown at the right.

 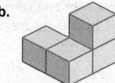

Number of cubes: 3

a.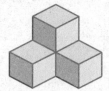

b.

c.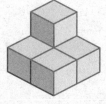

d.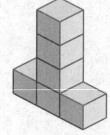

7.4 Notetaking with Vocabulary

Vocabulary:

Notes:

7.4 Self-Assessment

Use the scale below to rate your understanding of the learning target and the success criteria.

1	**2**	**3**	**4**
I do not understand.	I can do it with help.	I can do it on my own.	I can teach someone else.

	Rating	Date
7.4 Three-Dimensional Figures		
Learning Target: Describe and draw three-dimensional figures.	1 2 3 4	
I can find the numbers of faces, edges, and vertices of a three-dimensional figure.	1 2 3 4	
I can draw prisms and pyramids.	1 2 3 4	
I can draw the front, side, and top views of a three-dimensional figure.	1 2 3 4	

Practice

Draw the solid.

1. Octagonal pyramid

2. Octagonal prism

Draw the front, side, and top views of the solid.

3.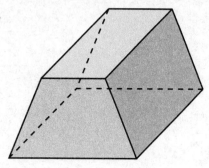

4.

Draw a solid with the following front, side, and top views.

5.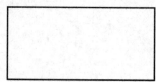

    front   side   top

6. Two of the three views of a solid are shown.

  front   top

    a. What is the greatest number of cubes in the solid?

    b. What is the least number of cubes in the solid?

    c. Draw the side views of both solids in parts (a) and (b).

7. The base of a prism has *n* sides. Find the numbers of faces, edges, and vertices of the prism. Explain your reasoning.

Name_____ Date_____

Learning Target: Represent prisms using nets and use nets to find surface areas of prisms.

Success Criteria:
- I can draw nets to represent prisms.
- I can use nets to find surface areas of prisms.
- I can use a formula to find the surface area of a cube.
- I can apply surface areas of prisms to solve real-life problems.

1 **EXPLORATION:** Using Grid Graph to Construct a Solid

Work with a partner. Copy the figure shown below onto grid paper (*).

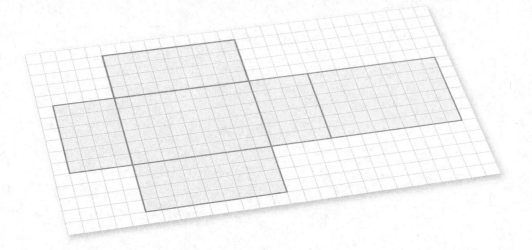

a. Cut out and fold the figure to form a solid. What type of solid does the figure form?

b. What is the area of the entire surface of the solid?

*Grid paper is available in the back of the Student Journal.

7.5 **Surface Areas of Prisms** (continued)

2 **EXPLORATION:** Finding the Area of the Entire Surface

Work with a partner. Find the area of the entire surface of each solid. Explain your reasoning.

a.
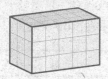

b.
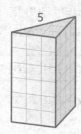
5

Name_____ Date _____

Vocabulary:

Notes:

7.5 **Self-Assessment**

Use the scale below to rate your understanding of the learning target and the success criteria.

1	2	3	4
I do not understand.	I can do it with help.	I can do it on my own.	I can teach someone else.

	Rating	Date
7.5 Surface Areas of Prisms		
Learning Target: Represent prisms using nets and use nets to find surface areas of prisms.	1 2 3 4	
I can draw nets to represent prisms.	1 2 3 4	
I can use nets to find surface areas of prisms.	1 2 3 4	
I can use a formula to find the surface area of a cube.	1 2 3 4	
I can apply surface areas of prisms to solve real-life problems.	1 2 3 4	

Name _____ Date _____

Find the surface area of the prism.

1.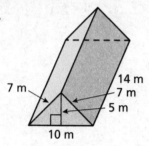

2.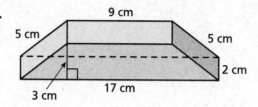

3. A cake recipe calls for a pan that is 9 inches by 11 inches by 2 inches.

   a. What is the surface area of the recipe's cake pan? (The top of the cake pan is open.)

   b. You have a cake pan that is 10 inches by 10 inches by 2 inches. What is the surface area of your cake pan? (The top of the cake pan is open.)

   c. Your friend has a cake pan with a right triangular base and a depth of 5 inches. The triangular base is a right triangle with both legs of length 10 inches and hypotenuse of length 14.15 inches. What is the surface area of your friend's cake pan? (The top of the cake pan is open.)

   d. The length of time that a cake bakes depends on the surface area and the depth of the cake pan. Will *you* or *your friend* need to adjust the length of time to bake your cake? Do you think the length of time will increase or decrease? Explain.

4. A company changed the packaging of their most popular product. The old packaging was a box in the shape of a rectangular prism measuring 1 in. by 2 in. by 8 in. The new packaging is a box in the shape of a rectangular prism measuring 1 in. by 4 in. by 4 in. The volume of the packaging has not changed.

   a. Why do you think the company would make this change in the appearance of the box? Does this appearance change the surface area of the packaging?

   b. The cost of the packaging increased 10%. Will the company spend *more*, *less*, or *the same* for packaging this product with the new packing size? Explain.

7.6 Surface Areas of Pyramids
For use with Exploration 7.6

Learning Target: Represent pyramids using nets and use nets to find the surface areas of pyramids.

Success Criteria: • I can draw nets to represent pyramids.
• I can use nets to find surface areas of pyramids.
• I can apply surface areas of pyramids to solve real-life problems.

1 EXPLORATION: Using a Net to Construct a Solid

Work with a partner. Copy the net shown below onto grid paper (*).

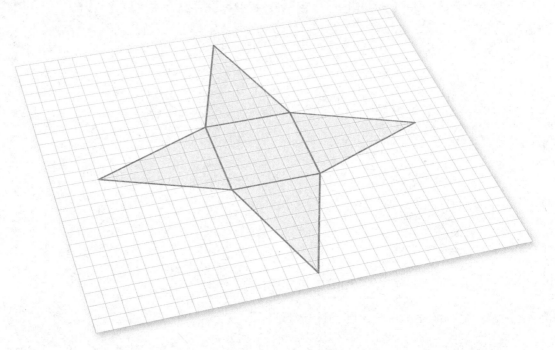

a. Cut out and fold the net to form a solid. What type of solid does the net form?

b. What is the surface area of the solid?

*Grid paper is available in the back of the Student Journal.

7.6 **Surface Areas of Pyramids** (continued)

---

2 **EXPLORATION:** Finding Surface Areas of Solids

Work with a partner. Find the surface area of each solid. Explain your reasoning.

a.

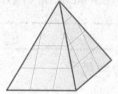

b.

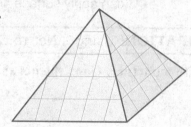

Notetaking with Vocabulary

Vocabulary:

Notes:

 Self-Assessment

Use the scale below to rate your understanding of the learning target and the success criteria.

1	2	3	4
I do not understand.	I can do it with help.	I can do it on my own.	I can teach someone else.

	Rating	Date
7.6 Surface Areas of Pyramids		
Learning Target: Represent pyramids using nets and use nets to find surface areas of pyramids.	1 2 3 4	
I can draw nets to represent pyramids.	1 2 3 4	
I can use nets to find surface areas of pyramids.	1 2 3 4	
I can apply surface areas of pyramids to solve real-life problems.	1 2 3 4	

7.6 Practice

Find the surface area of the pyramid.

1.

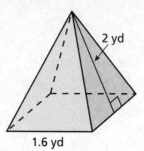

2 yd

1.6 yd

2.

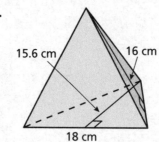

15.6 cm   16 cm

18 cm

3. The surface area of a triangular pyramid is
96.6 square centimeters. The side lengths of
the base are 6 centimeters, and the height of
the base is 5.2 centimeters. What is the value
of x?

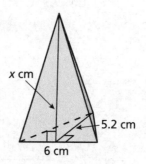

x cm

5.2 cm

6 cm

4. A pendant for earrings is designed in the shape of a square pyramid. The
pendant will be open on the bottom, and consist of an inner and an outer
square pyramid.

a. For the outer square pyramid, the side length of the base is 1.5
centimeters and the height of one of the triangular faces is 3 centimeters.
What is the surface area of the outer square pyramid?

b. The dimensions of the inner square pyramid have a ratio of 2 : 3 to the
dimensions of the outer square pyramid. What are the dimensions of the
inner square pyramid?

c. What is the ratio of the surface area of the inner square pyramid to the
surface area of the outer square pyramid? How does this compare to the
ratio of their dimensions: more, less, or about the same? Explain your
reasoning.

7.7 Volumes of Rectangular Prisms
For use with Exploration 7.7

Learning Target: Find volumes and missing dimensions of rectangular prisms.

Success Criteria:
- I can use a formula to find the volume of a rectangular prism.
- I can use a formula to find the volume of a cube.
- I can use the volume of a rectangular prism and two of its dimensions to find the other dimension.
- I can apply volumes of rectangular prisms to solve real-life problems.

---

1 EXPLORATION: Using a Unit Cube

Work with a partner. A *unit cube* is a cube with an edge length of 1 unit. The parallel edges of the unit cube have been divided into 2, 3, and 4 equal parts to create smaller rectangular prisms that are identical.

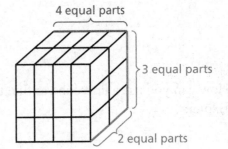

4 equal parts

3 equal parts

2 equal parts

a. The volumes of the identical prisms are equal. What else can you determine about the volumes of the prisms? Explain.

7.7 **Volumes of Rectangular Prisms** (continued)

b. Use the identical prisms in part (a) to find the volume of the prism below. Explain your reasoning.

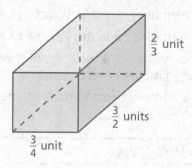

$\frac{2}{3}$ unit

$\frac{3}{2}$ units

$\frac{3}{4}$ unit

c. How can you use a unit cube to find the volume of the prism below? Explain.

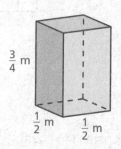

$\frac{3}{4}$ m

$\frac{1}{2}$ m $\frac{1}{2}$ m

d. Do the formulas $V = Bh$ and $V = \ell wh$ work for rectangular prisms with fractional edge lengths? Give examples to support your answer.

7.7 Notetaking with Vocabulary

Vocabulary:

Notes:

7.7 Self-Assessment

Use the scale below to rate your understanding of the learning target and the success criteria.

1	2	3	4
I do not understand.	I can do it with help.	I can do it on my own.	I can teach someone else.

	Rating	Date
7.7 Volumes of Rectangular Prisms		
Learning Target: Find volumes and missing dimensions of rectangular prisms.	1 2 3 4	
I can use a formula to find the volume of a rectangular prism.	1 2 3 4	
I can use a formula to find the volume of a cube.	1 2 3 4	
I can use the volume of a rectangular prism and two of its dimensions to find the other dimension.	1 2 3 4	
I can apply volumes of rectangular prisms to solve real-life problems.	1 2 3 4	

Big Ideas Math: Modeling Real Life Grade 6 **177**
Student Journal

7.7 Practice

1. A storage trunk is 3 feet long and 1 foot wide. The height of the trunk is $1\frac{1}{4}$ feet. What is the volume of the trunk?

2. A filing cabinet is 35 centimeters wide, 70 centimeters long, and 115 centimeters high. The bottom drawer is 30% of the volume of the filing cabinet. What is the height of the bottom drawer?

Find the missing dimension of the prism.

3. Volume = 220.8 mm^3

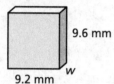

9.6 mm

9.2 mm w

4. Volume = $23\frac{1}{25}$ ft^3

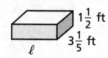

$1\frac{1}{2}$ ft

$3\frac{1}{5}$ ft

ℓ

5. Volume = $\frac{9}{125}$ mi^3

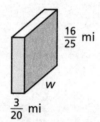

$\frac{16}{25}$ mi

w

$\frac{3}{20}$ mi

6. A cellular phone is in the shape of a rectangular prism. The height of the phone is 6 millimeters, and the width is 50 millimeters. The volume is 22,500 cubic millimeters. What is the length of the cellular phone?

7. A cube is made up of a group of smaller, identical cubes. The cube has a side length of six feet.

   a. What is the volume of one of the smaller cubes?

   b. Convert your answer in part (a) from cubic feet to cubic inches.

8. A calendar that has one page (i.e., one piece of paper) per day is 7 inches long, 7 inches wide, and 2 inches high.

   a. What is the volume of one page of the calendar? Round your answer to the nearest thousandth.

   b. What is the volume of the pages of the calendar for the month of July? Round your answer to the nearest thousandth.

9. What happens to the volume of a rectangular prism if you multiply the length, the width, and the height by 2?

Name_____ Date_____

Chapter 7 — Chapter Self-Assessment

Use the scale below to rate your understanding of the learning target and the success criteria.

1 I do not understand.

2 I can do it with help.

3 I can do it on my own.

4 I can teach someone else.

	Rating	Date
7.1 Areas of Parallelograms		
Learning Target: Find areas and missing dimensions of parallelograms.	1 2 3 4	
I can explain how the area of a rectangle is used to find the area of a parallelogram.	1 2 3 4	
I can use the base and the height of a parallelogram to find its area.	1 2 3 4	
I can use the area of a parallelogram and one of its dimensions to find the other dimension.	1 2 3 4	
7.2 Areas of Triangles		
Learning Target: Find areas and missing dimensions of triangles, and find areas of composite figures.	1 2 3 4	
I can explain how the area of a parallelogram is used to find the area of a triangle.	1 2 3 4	
I can use the base and the height of a triangle to find its area.	1 2 3 4	
I can use the area of a triangle and one of its dimensions to find the other dimension.	1 2 3 4	
I can use decomposition to find the area of a figure.	1 2 3 4	
7.3 Areas of Trapezoids and Kites		
Learning Target: Find areas of trapezoids, kites, and composite figures.	1 2 3 4	
I can explain how the area of a parallelogram is used to find the area of a trapezoid.	1 2 3 4	
I can decompose trapezoids and kites into smaller shapes.	1 2 3 4	
I can use decomposition to find the area of a figure.	1 2 3 4	
I can use the bases and the height of a trapezoid to find its area.	1 2 3 4	

Chapter 7 — Chapter Self-Assessment (continued)

	Rating	Date
7.4 Three-Dimensional Figures		
Learning Target: Describe and draw three-dimensional figures.	1 2 3 4	
I can find the numbers of faces, edges, and vertices of a three-dimensional figure.	1 2 3 4	
I can draw prisms and pyramids.	1 2 3 4	
I can draw the front, side, and top views of a three-dimensional figure.	1 2 3 4	
7.5 Surface Areas of Prisms		
Learning Target: Represent prisms using nets and use nets to find surface areas of prisms.	1 2 3 4	
I can draw nets to represent prisms.	1 2 3 4	
I can use nets to find surface areas of prisms.	1 2 3 4	
I can use a formula to find the surface area of a cube.	1 2 3 4	
I can apply surface areas of prisms to solve real-life problems.	1 2 3 4	
7.6 Surface Areas of Pyramids		
Learning Target: Represent pyramids using nets and use nets to find surface areas of pyramids.	1 2 3 4	
I can draw nets to represent pyramids.	1 2 3 4	
I can use nets to find surface areas of pyramids.	1 2 3 4	
I can apply surface areas of pyramids to solve real-life problems.	1 2 3 4	
7.7 Volumes of Rectangular Prisms		
Learning Target: Find volumes and missing dimensions of rectangular prisms.	1 2 3 4	
I can use a formula to find the volume of a rectangular prism.	1 2 3 4	
I can use a formula to find the volume of a cube.	1 2 3 4	
I can use the volume of a rectangular prism and two of its dimensions to find the other dimension.	1 2 3 4	
I can apply volumes of rectangular prisms to solve real-life problems.		

Chapter 8 **Review & Refresh**

Find the area of the square or rectangle.

1.

5 ft

10 ft

2.

3 cm

3 cm

3.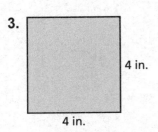

4 in.

4 in.

4.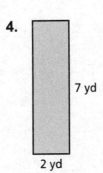

7 yd

2 yd

5. Find the area of the patio.

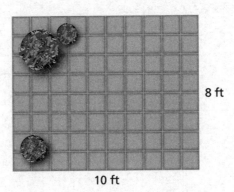

8 ft

10 ft

Chapter 8 **Review & Refresh** (continued)

Plot the ordered pair in a coordinate plane.

6. $(2, 3)$

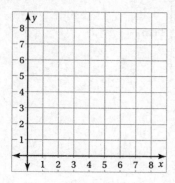

7. $(6, 5)$

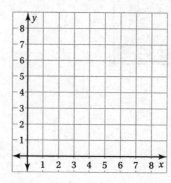

8. $(1, 7)$

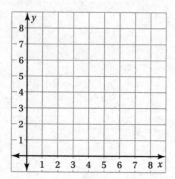

9. $(4, 4)$

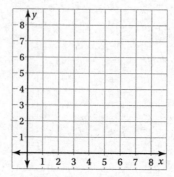

10. $(5, 2)$

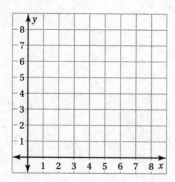

11. $(3, 1)$

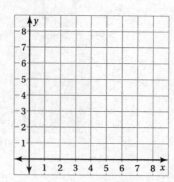

Name_____ Date _____

8.1 **Integers**
For use with Exploration 8.1

Learning Target: Understand the concept of negative numbers and that they are used along with positive numbers to describe quantities.

Success Criteria:
- I can write integers to represent quantities in real life.
- I can graph integers on a number line.
- I can find the opposite of an integer.
- I can apply integers to model real-life problems.

1 EXPLORATION: Reading and Describing Temperatures

Work with a partner. The thermometers show the temperatures in four cities.

Honolulu, Hawaii   *Anchorage, Alaska*

Death Valley, California   *Seattle, Washington*

a. Match each temperature with its most appropriate location.

8.1 **Integers** (continued)

  b. What do all of the temperatures have in common?

  c. What does it mean for a temperature to be *below* zero? Provide an example. Can you think of any other situations in which numbers may be less than zero?

  d. The thermometers show temperatures on a vertical number line. How else can you represent numbers less than zero? Provide an example.

Name_____ Date_____

 8.1 **Notetaking with Vocabulary**

Vocabulary:

Notes:

8.1 **Self-Assessment**

Use the scale below to rate your understanding of the learning target and
the success criteria.

1	*2*	*3*	*4*
I do not understand.	I can do it with help.	I can do it on my own.	I can teach someone else.

	Rating	Date
8.1 Integers		
Learning Target: Understand the concept of negative numbers and that they are used along with positive numbers to describe quantities.	1 2 3 4	
I can write integers to represent quantities in real life.	1 2 3 4	
I can graph integers on a number line.	1 2 3 4	
I can find the opposite of an integer.	1 2 3 4	
I can apply integers to model real-life problems.	1 2 3 4	

8.1 Practice

Write a positive or negative integer that represents the situation.

1. You run up 24 steps.

2. You give away 2 of your video games.

Graph the integer and its opposite.

3. −45   4. 250   5. −200

6. You roll a number cube and move ahead 3 spaces. Your friend rolls a number cube and moves the opposite of your move. Graph both moves.

Identify the integer represented by the point on the number line.

7. A   8. B   9. C   10. D

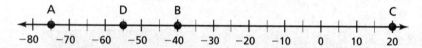

11. Use the information below to write an integer that represents your height on the teeter totter relative to the balance point height.

    a. You are 8 inches below the balance point height.

    b. From where you are in part (a), you go up 23 inches.

    c. Your friend is 12 inches above the balance point height. Your height is the opposite.

    d. You are resting at the balance point height.

12. You are riding a roller coaster. During the ride, you climb 25 feet, descend 30 feet, climb 50 feet, and then descend 55 feet. Do you finish *above*, *below*, or at the *same* height as you started? Explain.

13. Your friend thinks that the integer −n is a negative integer.

    a. Is your friend *always*, *sometimes*, or *never* correct? Explain your reasoning.

    b. Is your friend correct when n = 0? Explain.

Name_____ Date_____

8.2 Comparing and Ordering Integers
For use with Exploration 8.2

Learning Target: Compare and order integers.

Success Criteria:
- I can explain how to determine which of two integers is greater.
- I can order a set of integers from least to greatest.
- I can interpret statements about order in real-life problems.

1 EXPLORATION: Seconds to Liftoff

Work with a partner. You are listening to a command center before the liftoff of a rocket.

You hear the following:

"T minus 10 seconds...go for main engine start...T minus 9...
8...7...6...5...4...3...2...1...we have liftoff."

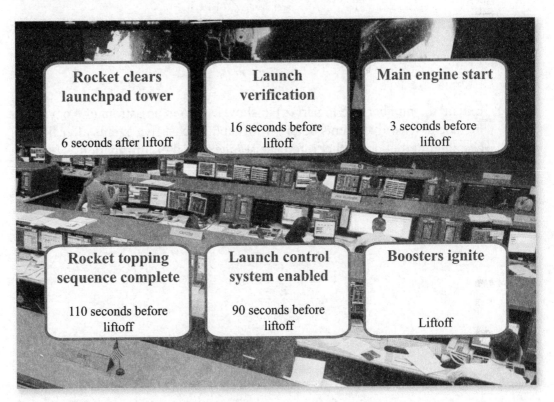

Rocket clears launchpad tower
6 seconds after liftoff

Launch verification
16 seconds before liftoff

Main engine start
3 seconds before liftoff

Rocket topping sequence complete
110 seconds before liftoff

Launch control system enabled
90 seconds before liftoff

Boosters ignite
Liftoff

a. Represent these events on a number line.

8.2 **Comparing and Ordering Integers** (continued)

b. List the events in the order they occurred. Explain your reasoning.

c. Extend the number line in part (a) to show events in an astronaut's day. Include at least five events before liftoff and at least five events after liftoff. Use the Internet or another reference source to gather information.

Name_____ Date _____

 8.2 **Notetaking with Vocabulary**

Vocabulary:

Notes:

8.2 **Self-Assessment**

Use the scale below to rate your understanding of the learning target and the success criteria.

1	*2*	*3*	*4*
I do not understand.	I can do it with help.	I can do it on my own.	I can teach someone else.

	Rating	Date
8.2 Comparing and Ordering Integers		
Learning Target: Compare and order integers.	1 2 3 4	
I can explain how to determine which of two integers is greater.	1 2 3 4	
I can order a set of integers from least to greatest.	1 2 3 4	
I can interpret statements about order in real-life problems.	1 2 3 4	

8.2 Practice

Order the integers from least to greatest.

1. 20, –20, 40, 50, –50

2. 10, –15, –20, 25, –30

3. In a round of golf, the lowest score wins. At the end of a round you have score –3 and your friend has score −4. Who won the round? Explain.

4. Seven integers are ordered from least to greatest. The integer in the middle is zero. Describe the other six numbers.

5. The table shows the highest and lowest daily profit/loss of the five locations of a chain of restaurants.

Location	Highest Profit/Loss	Lowest Profit/Loss
North	350	125
South	275	–50
East	300	–100
West	50	–250
Central	225	75

   a. Order the locations by their highest profit/loss from least to greatest.

   b. Order the locations by their lowest profit/loss from least to greatest.

   c. Find the middle integer of the highest profit/loss.

   d. Find the middle integer of the lowest profit/loss.

   e. The company needs to close one of the locations. Which location should they close? Explain.

6. Point A is on a number line halfway between –20 and −4. Point B is halfway between point A and 0. What integer is represented by point B?

7. Nine Celsius temperatures are recorded in a lab. The middle temperature is 0°C. What is the maximum number of temperatures that could be represented by negative numbers?

Tell whether the statement is *always*, *sometimes*, or *never* true. Explain your answer.

8. The opposite of a negative integer is less than zero.

9. An integer is to the right of its opposite on the number line.

8.3 Rational Numbers
For use with Exploration 8.3

Learning Target: Compare and order rational numbers.

Success Criteria:
- I can explain the meaning of a rational number.
- I can graph rational numbers on a number line.
- I can determine which of two rational numbers if greater.
- I can order a set of rational numbers from least to greatest.

---

1 EXPLORATION: Locating Fractions on a Number Line

Work with a partner. Represent the events on a number line using a fraction or a mixed number.

   a. Radio Transmission: 11:30 A.M.   **b.** Space Walk: 7:30 P.M.

   c. Physical Exam: 4:45 A.M.   **d.** Take Photograph: 3:15 A.M.

8.3 **Rational Numbers** (continued)

    e. Float in the Cabin: 6:20 P.M.   **f.** Eat Dinner: 8:40 P.M.

Name_____ Date_____

8.3 Notetaking with Vocabulary

Vocabulary:

Notes:

8.3 Self-Assessment

Use the scale below to rate your understanding of the learning target and the success criteria.

1	2	3	4
I do not understand.	I can do it with help.	I can do it on my own.	I can teach someone else.

	Rating	Date
8.3 Rational Numbers		
Learning Target: Compare and order rational numbers.	1 2 3 4	
I can explain the meaning of a rational number.	1 2 3 4	
I can graph rational numbers on a number line.	1 2 3 4	
I can determine which of two rational numbers is greater.	1 2 3 4	
I can order a set of rational numbers from least to greatest.	1 2 3 4	

Name_____ Date _____

8.3 Practice

Find a fraction or mixed number that is between the two numbers.

1.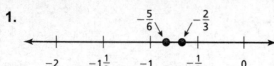

2.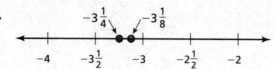

Complete the statement using < or >.

3. $-1\frac{2}{3}$ ____ $-1\frac{1}{2}$

4. -2.05 ____ -2.50

Order the numbers from least to greatest.

5. $-\frac{5}{8}, -\frac{3}{4}, -1\frac{1}{8}, -\frac{3}{8}, -1\frac{1}{4}$

6. $0.7, -0.3, 0, 0.25, -0.37$

7. Two runners slow down. One decelerates at $-\frac{5}{8}$ ft/sec² and the second at $-\frac{3}{5}$ ft/sec². Which runner slowed down more?

8. In physics, positive speeds denote upward motion and negative speeds denote downward motion. The table gives the speed of a ball thrown upward at a rate of 20.0 meters per second.

Time (seconds)	0	1	2	3	4
Speed (meters/second)	20.0	10.2	0.4	–9.4	–19.2

a. When was the speed greatest going upward?

b. When was the speed greatest going downward?

c. Between what two times was the speed zero? What does a speed of 0 mean?

d. Between what two times did the ball start the downward motion? Explain.

9. A stock lost value on both Monday and Tuesday. On Monday, it changed by –5.7 points, and on Tuesday it changed by –3.8 points. On which day did it drop the least?

10. What integer values of x make the statement $x + (-x) = 0$ true?

Name_____ Date_____

Learning Target: Understand the concept of absolute value.

Success Criteria:
- I can find the absolute value of a number.
- I can make comparisons that involve absolute values of numbers.
- I can apply absolute value in real-life problems.

1 EXPLORATION: Comparing Positions of Objects

Work with a partner. The diagram shows the positions of several objects.

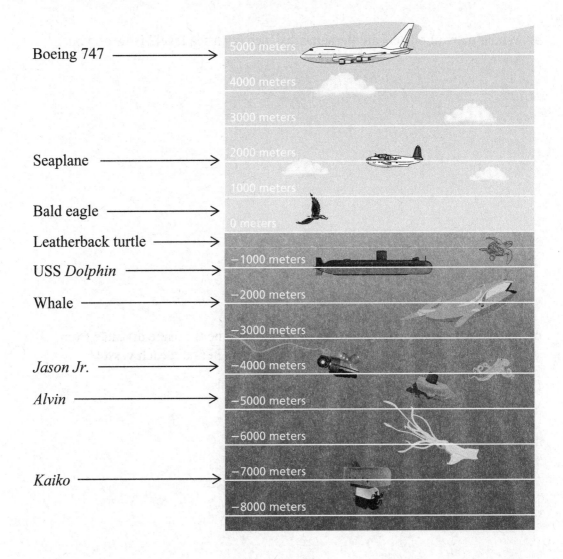

8.4 Absolute Value (continued)

a. What integer represents sea level? How can you compare the positions of objects relative to sea level?

b. Which pairs of objects are the same distance from sea level? How do you know?

c. The vessels *Kaiko*, *Alvin*, and *Jason Jr.* move to be the same distance from sea level as the Boeing 747. About how many meters did each vessel travel?

Name_____ Date _____

 8.4 **Notetaking with Vocabulary**

Vocabulary:

Notes:

 8.4 **Self-Assessment**

Use the scale below to rate your understanding of the learning target and the success criteria.

1	2	3	4
I do not understand.	I can do it with help.	I can do it on my own.	I can teach someone else.

	Rating	Date
8.4 Absolute Value		
Learning Target: Understand the concept of absolute value.	1 2 3 4	
I can find the absolute value of a number.	1 2 3 4	
I can make comparisons that involve absolute values of numbers.	1 2 3 4	
I can apply absolute value in real-life problems.	1 2 3 4	

8.4 Practice

Find the absolute value.

1. $\left|-\frac{1}{4}\right|$

2. $|-10.2|$

3. $\left|2\frac{1}{7}\right|$

4. Write two integers that have an absolute value of 15.

Complete the statement using <, >, or =.

5. $|9|$ ___ $|-9|$

6. $\left|-\frac{1}{6}\right|$ ___ $\left|\frac{1}{2}\right|$

7. Boat A and Boat B lie at the bottom of the ocean. In relation to sea level, the position of Boat A is –33 feet, and the position of Boat B is –25 feet.

   a. Find the absolute value of each position.

   b. Which boat is closer to sea level?

   c. Boat C also lies at the bottom of the ocean, and is located 28 feet below sea level. What is the position of Boat C?

Order the values from least to greatest.

8. 12, $|-13|$, –9, –12, $|-7|$, 0

9. $|20|$, $|-18|$, –15, $|-16|$, 22, –17

10. The word *ROTATOR* is a palindrome.

    a. Graph and label the following points on a number line: T = –2, A = 0; R = –6. Then, graph and label the absolute value of each point on the *same* number line.

    b. Assign a value to point O so that the letters spell the word *ROTATOR*. Then, graph point O and the absolute value of point O on the *same* number line as part (a).

11. Find values of x and y so that $|x| > |y|$ and $x < y$.

Tell whether the statement is *always*, *sometimes*, or *never* true.

12. The absolute value of a negative number is its opposite.

13. The opposite of the absolute value of a negative number is positive.

14. The opposite of the absolute value of a positive number is negative.

15. The absolute value of a number is less than the number.

Name_____ Date_____

8.5 The Coordinate Plane
For use with Exploration 8.5

Learning Target: Plot and reflect ordered pairs in all four quadrants of a coordinate plane.

Success Criteria:
- I can identify ordered pairs in a coordinate plane.
- I can plot ordered pairs in a coordinate plane and describe their locations.
- I can reflect points in the *x*-axis, the *y*-axis, or both axes.
- I can apply plotting points in all four quadrants to solve real-life problems.

1 EXPLORATION: Extending the Coordinate Plane

Work with a partner. Previously, you plotted points with positive coordinates in a coordinate plane like the one shown at the right.

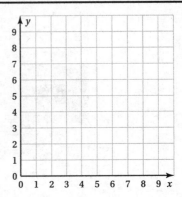

a. You can also plot points in which one or both of the coordinates are negative numbers. Create ordered pairs with different combinations of positive and negative coordinates, as described below. Then plot the ordered pairs and explain how you extended the coordinate plane shown.

  (positive, positive)   (negative, positive)

  (negative, negative)   (positive, negative)

8.5 **The Coordinate Plane** (continued)

b. How many regions of the coordinate plane are created by the *x*-axis and *y*-axis? What do the points in each of these regions have in common?

c. The photo shows the *reflection*, or mirror image, of a mountain in a lake. When you fold the photo on its axis, the mountain and its reflection align.

Actual mountain

Axis

Reflection of mountain

Plot a point and its *reflection* in one of the axes. Explain your reasoning. What do you notice about the coordinates of the points?

Notetaking with Vocabulary

Vocabulary:

Notes:

 Self-Assessment

Use the scale below to rate your understanding of the learning target and the success criteria.

1	2	3	4
I do not understand.	I can do it with help.	I can do it on my own.	I can teach someone else.

	Rating	Date
8.5 The Coordinate Plane		
Learning Target: Plot and reflect ordered pairs in all four quadrants of a coordinate plane.	1 2 3 4	
I can identify ordered pairs in a coordinate plane.	1 2 3 4	
I can plot ordered pairs in a coordinate plane and describe their locations.	1 2 3 4	
I can reflect points in the x-axis, the y-axis, or both axes.	1 2 3 4	
I can apply plotting points in all four quadrants to solve real-life problems.	1 2 3 4	

8.5 Practice

Write an ordered pair corresponding to the point.

1. Point *A*

2. Point *B*

3. Point *C*

4. Point *D*

5. Point *E*

6. Point *F*

7. Point *G*

8. Point *H*

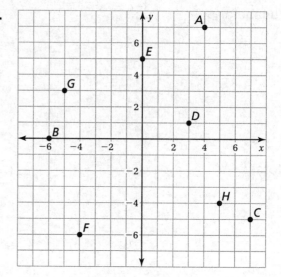

Tell whether the statement is *sometimes*, *always*, or *never* true. Explain.

9. The *y*-coordinate of points in Quadrant IV are positive.

10. A point with an *x*-coordinate of zero and a positive *y*-coordinate lies on the *y*-axis between Quadrants III and IV.

11. Two points, one with a positive *y*-coordinate and another with a negative *x*-coordinate, both lie in Quadrant II.

12. The points $P(2, 1)$, $Q(2, -3)$, $R(-1, -3)$ and $S(-1, 1)$ are vertices of a figure.

    a. Draw the figure in a coordinate plane.

    b. Find the perimeter of the figure.

    c. Find the area of the figure.

13. A movie theater is located at (a, b).

    a. To get from your house to the movie theater, you walk 4 blocks east and then 5 blocks north. What ordered pair corresponds to the location of your house?

    b. After walking 6 blocks on the path to the movie theater as described in part (a), you meet your friend at your friend's house. What ordered pair corresponds to the location of your friend's house?

    c. There are two ice cream parlors, one located at $(a - 1, b - 1)$ and another located at $(a - 2, b - 2)$. After a movie and ice cream, you will each walk home alone. Which location is most advantageous to both you and your friend?

    d. Choose a value for *a* between 0 and 2, and a value for *b* between 6 and 8. Use these values to determine the locations of the movie theater, your house, your friend's house, and the ice cream parlor.

8.6

Polygons in the Coordinate Plane
For use with Exploration 8.6

Learning Target: Draw polygons in the coordinate plane and find distances between points in the coordinate plane.

Success Criteria:
- I can draw polygons in the coordinate plane.
- I can find distances between points in the coordinate plane with the same *x*-coordinates or the same *y*-coordinates.
- I can find horizontal and vertical side lengths of polygons in the coordinate plane.
- I can draw polygons in the coordinate plane to solve real-life problems.

---

1 EXPLORATION: Drawing Polygons in the Coordinate Plane

Work with a partner.

a. Write three ordered pairs that meet the following requirements. Then plot the ordered pairs in a coordinate plane, like the one shown.

Two of the ordered pairs have the same *x*-coordinates.

Two of the ordered pairs have the same *y*-coordinates.

Two of the points are in the same quadrant. The other point is in a different quadrant.

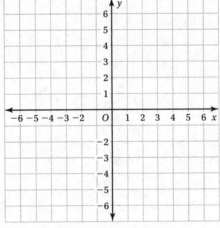

8.6 **Polygons in the Coordinate Plane** (continued)

b. The points represent the vertices of a polygon. What conclusions can you make about the polygon?

c. Can you plot another point to form a rectangle? a trapezoid? If so, what measures of the quadrilateral can you calculate?

8.6 Notetaking with Vocabulary

Vocabulary:

Notes:

8.6 Self-Assessment

Use the scale below to rate your understanding of the learning target and the success criteria.

1	2	3	4
I do not understand.	I can do it with help.	I can do it on my own.	I can teach someone else.

	Rating	Date
8.6 Polygons in the Coordinate Plane		
Learning Target: Draw polygons in the coordinate plane and find distances between points in the coordinate plane.	1 2 3 4	
I can draw polygons in the coordinate plane.	1 2 3 4	
I can find distances between points in the coordinate plane with the same x-coordinates or the same y-coordinates.	1 2 3 4	
I can find horizontal and vertical side lengths of polygons in the coordinate plane.	1 2 3 4	
I can draw polygons in the coordinate plane to solve real-life problems.	1 2 3 4	

8.6 Practice

Draw the polygon with the given vertices in a coordinate plane.

1. $D(2,4), E\left(2,5\frac{1}{2}\right), F\left(7,5\frac{1}{2}\right), G(7,4)$

2. $M\left(1\frac{1}{2},5\right), N(4,7), P(7,3), Q(7,1), R(4,0)$

Find the perimeter and area of the polygon with the given vertices.

3. $C(-4,1), D(-4,-6), E(9,-6), F(9,1)$

4. $S(-8,4), T(4,4), U(4,7), V(-8,7)$

5. Describe and correct the error in drawing a rectangle with vertices $E(1,2), F(6,2), G(6,4), H(1,4)$.

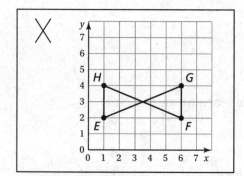

Draw a polygon with the given conditions in a coordinate plane.

6. A rectangle with a perimeter of 22 units, an area of 24 units, and located in Quadrants II and III

7. A triangle with an area of 21 square units with vertices in three different quadrants

8. You use a coordinate plane to plot the two bus routes that you can take from your house to your school. You plot your house at $A(5, 5)$ and the school at $C(24, 20)$. The first route includes one bus stop at $B(5, 20)$. The second route includes 3 bus stops at $D(24, 15)$, $E(20, 15)$, and $F(20, 5)$. Which route has the shorter distance? Explain.

9. The vertices of a rectangle are (a, b), $(2a, b)$, $(2a, 2b)$, and $(a, 2b)$. The values of a and b are both positive.

   a. For $a = 1$ and $b = 1$, what is the perimeter of the rectangle?

   b. For $a = 2$ and $b = 3$, what is the perimeter of the rectangle?

   c. What is the perimeter of the rectangle in terms of a and b?

Name_____ Date_____

Writing and Graphing Inequalities
8.7
For use with Exploration 8.7

Learning Target: Write inequalities and represent solutions of inequalities on number lines.

Success Criteria:
- I can write word sentences as inequalities.
- I can determine whether a value is a solution of an inequality.
- I can graph the solutions of inequalities.

1 EXPLORATION: Understanding Inequality Statements

Work with a partner. Create a number line on the floor with both positive and negative integers.

  a. For each statement, stand at a number on your number line that makes the statement true. On what other numbers can you stand?

Class starts more than 3 minutes late.

You need at least 3 peaches for a recipe.

The temperature is at most 3 degrees Celsius.

After playing a video game for 5 minutes, you have fewer than 3 points.

Name _____ Date _____

b. How can you represent the solutions of each statement in part (a) on a
number line?

Name_____ Date_____

8.7 Notetaking with Vocabulary

Vocabulary:

Notes:

8.7 Self-Assessment

Use the scale below to rate your understanding of the learning target and the success criteria.

1	2	3	4
I do not understand.	I can do it with help.	I can do it on my own.	I can teach someone else.

	Rating	Date
8.7 Writing and Graphing Inequalities		
Learning Target: Write inequalities and represent solutions of inequalities on number lines.	1 2 3 4	
I can write word sentences as inequalities.	1 2 3 4	
I can determine whether a value is a solution of an inequality.	1 2 3 4	
I can graph the solutions of inequalities.	1 2 3 4	

Name _____ Date _____

Write the word sentence as an inequality.

1. A number b times 3.5 is no less than 21.

2. The difference between a number h and $\frac{1}{4}$ is at most 0.

3. The sum of a number w and 2.56 is at least 10.24.

Write an inequality and a word sentence that represent the graph.

4. 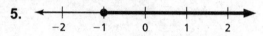 5.

Graph the inequality on a number line.

6. $-18 \geq s$ 7. $w < -56.8$ 8. $n > \frac{7}{5}$

9. A highway passes under a road. The clearance height is 17.75 feet.

   a. Write and graph an inequality that represents the height of a vehicle that can travel on the highway.

   b. The top of the flat bed on a truck is 4.25 feet above the ground. Write an inequality that represents the height of what can be carried on the flat bed as the truck travels on the highway.

10. You must be at least 48 inches tall to go on the Scrambler at an amusement park. You must be at most 48 inches tall to go on the Busy Boats at the park.

    a. Write an inequality that represents the height you must be for each of the rides.

    b. You are allowed to ride both rides. What is your height?

11. State the integers that are solutions of both of the following inequalities:

    a. $n \leq 8$ and $n > 2$.

    b. $n > -4$ and $n < -2$

    c. $n \leq -5$ and $n > 7$

    d. $n > 10$ and $n \leq 10$

    e. $n \leq -11$ and $n \geq -11$

Solving Inequalities
For use with Exploration 8.8

Learning Target: Write and solve inequalities.

Success Criteria:
- I can apply the properties of inequality to generate equivalent inequalities.
- I can solve inequalities using addition or subtraction.
- I can solve inequalities using multiplication or division.
- I can write and solve inequalities that represent real-life problems.

---

1 EXPLORATION: Using Tape Diagrams

Work with a partner. In Section 6.2 Exploration 1, the tape diagram below was used to model the equation $x + 4 = 12$.

12

x	4

a. Suppose that $x + 4$ is greater than 12. How can you change the equation to represent the new relationship between $x + 4$ and 12?

b. A student finds the possible values of x using the tape diagrams below. What is the solution? How can you find the solution algebraically?

12

4	x

4	8

4	x

8

x

8.8 **Solving Inequalities** (continued)

c. Describe the relationship between $4x$ and 20 as shown by the tape diagram below. What can you conclude about x?

20

4x

8.8 Notetaking with Vocabulary

Vocabulary:

Notes:

8.8 Self-Assessment

Use the scale below to rate your understanding of the learning target and the success criteria.

1	2	3	4
I do not understand.	I can do it with help.	I can do it on my own.	I can teach someone else.

	Rating	Date
8.8 Solving Inequalities		
Learning Target: Write and solve inequalities.	1 2 3 4	
I can apply the properties of inequality to generate equivalent inequalities.	1 2 3 4	
I can solve inequalities using addition or subtraction.	1 2 3 4	
I can solve inequalities using multiplication or division.	1 2 3 4	
I can write and solve inequalities that represent real-life problems.	1 2 3 4	

Name_____ Date _____

8.8 Practice

Solve the inequality. Graph the solution. Find two integers that are solutions to the inequality.

1. $9\frac{1}{4} < z - 4\frac{1}{8}$

2. $u + \frac{1}{3} \le \frac{1}{2}$

3. $h - 3.1 > 1.3$

4. $7.2p > 64.8$

5. $\frac{k}{2} < \frac{7}{20}$

6. $\frac{6n}{5} < 9$

Write the word sentence as an inequality. Then solve the inequality.

7. 9.1 less than a number is less than 4.6.

8. 10 times a number q is at least 2.01.

9. $5\frac{1}{4}$ is greater than a number plus $2\frac{1}{10}$.

10. A number d divided by 8 is no more than 3.43.

Graph the numbers that are solutions to both inequalities.

11. $y - 2 > 5$ and $6y \le 60$

12. $p + 6 \ge 11$ and $3p < 18$

13. $3m \ge 12$ and $\frac{m}{2} > 3$

14. $x - 10 < 0$ and $\frac{x}{4} \le 1$

15. The possible values of x are given by $x + 2.1 \le 6.5$. What is the greatest possible value of $\frac{x}{4}$?

16. Three friends decide to share the cost to rent an apartment equally. The apartments that they are considering cost at least $1200 per month. Write and solve an inequality to represent each person's share of the rental cost.

17. A printer can print up to 80 pages a minute.

   a. Write and solve an inequality to represent the number of minutes required to print a report of 380 pages.

   b. Write and solve an inequality to represent the number of minutes required to print 15 reports of 380 pages each.

   c. Write and solve an inequality to represent the number of hours required to print a document of 15,000 pages.

Name_____ Date_____

Chapter Self-Assessment

Use the scale below to rate your understanding of the learning target and the success criteria.

1	*2*	*3*	*4*
I do not understand.	I can do it with help.	I can do it on my own.	I can teach someone else.

	Rating	Date
8.1 Integers		
Learning Target: Understand the concept of negative numbers and that they are used along with positive numbers to describe quantities.	1 2 3 4	
I can write integers to represent quantities in real life.	1 2 3 4	
I can graph integers on a number line.	1 2 3 4	
I can find the opposite of an integer.	1 2 3 4	
I can apply integers to model real-life problems.	1 2 3 4	
8.2 Comparing and Ordering Integers		
Learning Target: Compare and order integers	1 2 3 4	
I can explain how to determine which of two integers is greater.	1 2 3 4	
I can order a set of integers from least to greatest.	1 2 3 4	
I can interpret statements about order in real-life problems.	1 2 3 4	
8.3 Rational Numbers		
Learning Target: Compare and order rational numbers.	1 2 3 4	
I can explain the meaning of a rational number.	1 2 3 4	
I can graph rational numbers on a number line.	1 2 3 4	
I can determine which of two rational numbers is greater.	1 2 3 4	
I can order a set of rational numbers from least to greatest.	1 2 3 4	
8.4 Absolute Value		
Learning Target: Understand the concept of absolute value.	1 2 3 4	
I can find the absolute value of a number.	1 2 3 4	
I can make comparisons that involve absolute values of numbers.	1 2 3 4	
I can apply absolute value in real-life problems.	1 2 3 4	

Name _____ Date _____

	Rating	Date
8.5 The Coordinate Plane		
Learning Target: Plot and reflect ordered pairs in all four quadrants of a coordinate plane.	1 2 3 4	
I can identify ordered pairs in a coordinate plane.	1 2 3 4	
I can plot ordered pairs in a coordinate plane and describe their locations.	1 2 3 4	
I can reflect points in the x-axis, the y-axis, or both axes.	1 2 3 4	
I can apply plotting points in all four quadrants to solve real-life problems.	1 2 3 4	
8.6 Polygons in the Coordinate Plane		
Learning Target: Draw polygons in the coordinate plane and find distances between points in the coordinate plane.	1 2 3 4	
I can draw polygons in the coordinate plane.	1 2 3 4	
I can find distances between points in the coordinate plane with the same x-coordinates or the same y-coordinates.	1 2 3 4	
I can find horizontal and vertical side lengths of polygons in the coordinate plane.	1 2 3 4	
I can draw polygons in the coordinate plane to solve real-life problems.	1 2 3 4	
8.7 Writing and Graphing Inequalities		
Learning Target: Write inequalities and represent solutions of inequalities on number lines.	1 2 3 4	
I can write word sentences as inequalities.	1 2 3 4	
I can determine whether a value is a solution of an inequality.	1 2 3 4	
I can graph the solutions of inequalities.	1 2 3 4	
8.8 Solving Inequalities		
Learning Target: Write and solve inequalities.	1 2 3 4	
I can apply the properties of inequality to generate equivalent inequalities.	1 2 3 4	
I can solve inequalities using addition or subtraction.	1 2 3 4	
I can solve inequalities using multiplication or division.	1 2 3 4	
I can write and solve inequalities that represent real-life problems.	1 2 3 4	

Name_____ Date _____

Chapter 9 Review & Refresh

Use a number line to order the numbers from least to greatest.

1. 1.5, 4.5, 5, 2.5, 1, 3

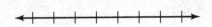

2. 6, 3.5, 4, 5.5, 7.5, 4.5

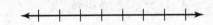

3. 5.25, 6, 3.5, 5, 6.25, 4.25

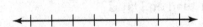

4. 4.75, 6.5, 7, 7.75, 5.5, 3

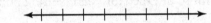

5. 3.25, 5.75, 4.5, 3.75, 4.25, 6.5

6. 3.75, 1.5, 4.75, 1.25, 2.25, 3.5

Review & Refresh (continued)

In Exercises 7-9, use the double bar graph that shows the sales of a clothing store over two days.

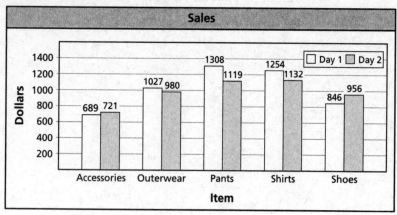

7. How much more did the store earn selling shirts on Day 1 than on Day 2?

8. Which item had the largest change in sales?

9. Which item had the highest sales total for the two days?

9.1 Introduction to Statistics
For use with Exploration 9.1

Learning Target: Identify statistical questions and use data to answer statistical questions.

Success Criteria:
- I can recognize questions that anticipate a variety of answers.
- I can construct and interpret a dot plot.
- I can use data to answer a statistical question.

---

1 EXPLORATION: Using Data to Answer a Question

Work with a partner.

a. Use your pulse to find your heart rate in beats per minute.

b. Collect the recorded heart rates of the students in your class, including yourself. How spread out are the data? Use a diagram to justify your answer.

c. How would you answer the following question by using only one value? Explain your reasoning.

"What is the heart rate of a sixth-grade student?"

9.1 **Introduction to Statistics** (continued)

2 **EXPLORATION:** Identifying Types of Questions

Work with a partner.

a. Answer each question on your own. Then compare your answers with your partner's answers. For which questions should your answers be the same? For which questions might your answers be different?

1. How many states are in the United States?

2. How much does a movie ticket cost?

3. What color fur do bears have?

4. How tall is your math teacher?

b. Some of the questions in part (a) are considered *statistical* questions. Which ones are they? Explain.

Notetaking with Vocabulary

Vocabulary:

Notes:

 Self-Assessment

Use the scale below to rate your understanding of the learning target and the success criteria.

1	2	3	4
I do not understand.	I can do it with help.	I can do it on my own.	I can teach someone else.

	Rating	Date
9.1 Introduction to Statistics		
Learning Target: Identify statistical questions and use data to answer statistical questions.	1 2 3 4	
I can recognize questions that anticipate a variety of answers.	1 2 3 4	
I can construct and interpret a dot plot.	1 2 3 4	
I can use data to answer a statistical question.	1 2 3 4	

9.1 Practice

Determine whether the question is a statistical question. Explain.

1. How long did you wait in line?

2. How many games did you bowl?

3. How many quarters are in a football game?

Display the data in a dot plot. Identify any clusters, peaks, or gaps in the data.

4.

Number of Emails			
12	15	16	14
2	17	18	13
45	19	16	16

5.

Number of Ounces			
12	20	12	12
20	32	12	32
20	12	12	20

6. The dot plot shows the lengths of racing boats.

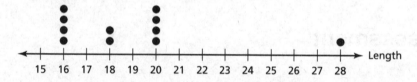

a. How many racing boats are represented?

b. How can you collect this data? What are the units?

c. Write a statistical question that you can answer using the dot plot. Then answer the question.

7. The results of a survey are shown.

a. Is this a statistical question? Explain.

b. Display the data in a dot plot. Identify any clusters, peaks or gaps in the data.

c. Use the distribution of the data to answer the question.

How many customers did you serve at lunch today?			
25	24	22	20
23	24	25	24
21	25	22	31
25	27	23	30

Name_____ Date _____

9.2 Mean
For use with Exploration 9.2

Learning Target: Find and interpret the mean of a data set.

Success Criteria:
- I can explain how the mean summarizes a data set with a single number.
- I can find the mean of a data set.
- I can use the mean of a data set to answer a statistical question.

1 **EXPLORATION: Finding a Balance Point**

Work with a partner. The diagrams show the numbers of tokens brought to a batting cage. Where on the number line is the data set *balanced*? Is this a good representation of the average? Explain.

a.

b.

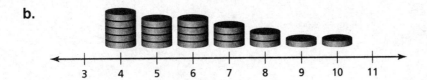

9.2   **Mean** (continued)

2   **EXPLORATION:** Finding a Fair Share

Work with a partner. One token lets you hit 12 baseballs in a batting cage. The table shows the numbers of tokens six friends bring to the batting cage.

Tokens					
John	**Lisa**	**Miguel**	**Matt**	**Cheryl**	**Anika**
6	3	4	5	2	4

   a. Regroup the tokens so that everyone has the same amount. How many times can each friend use the batting cage? Explain how this represents a "fair share".

   b. How can you find the answer in part (a) algebraically?

   c. Write a statistical question that can be answered using the value in part (a).

9.2 Notetaking with Vocabulary

Vocabulary:

Notes:

9.2 Self-Assessment

Use the scale below to rate your understanding of the learning target and the success criteria.

1	2	3	4
I do not understand.	I can do it with help.	I can do it on my own.	I can teach someone else.

	Rating	Date
9.2 Mean		
Learning Target: Find and interpret the mean of a data set.	1 2 3 4	
I can explain how the mean summarizes a data set with a single number.	1 2 3 4	
I can find the mean of a data set.	1 2 3 4	
I can use the mean of a data set to answer a statistical question.	1 2 3 4	

Name _____ Date _____

Find the mean of the data. Does the mean describe an average value of the data? Explain.

1. 34, 101, 255, 87, 66, 75, 222

2. 0.34, 0.27, 0.11, 0.45, 0.32, 0.29, 0.32

3. 62.0, 62.8, 62.1, 62.8, 62.2, 62.3, 62.4, 62.8

4. Compare your mean test scores for your science and math classes.

   Science: 88, 96, 93, 99   Math: 91, 92, 96

5. The body temperatures (in degrees Fahrenheit) of some students are shown.

   a. Which data value is an outlier? Explain.

   b. Find the mean with and without the outlier. Then describe how the outlier affects the mean.

   c. Describe a situation that could have caused the outlier in the problem.

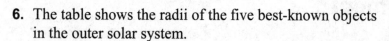

6. The table shows the radii of the five best-known objects in the outer solar system.

   a. Which data value is an outlier? Explain.

   b. Find the mean with and without the outlier. Describe how the outlier affects the mean.

   c. Look up information about the outer solar system. Based on how the five objects are classified, do you think that an average of the data has more meaning *with* the outlier or *without* it? Explain your reasoning.

Object	Radius (km)
Jupiter	71,492
Saturn	60,268
Uranus	25,559
Neptune	24,764
Pluto	1151

7. There are six boys and six girls in a class. The mean height of the girls is 59 inches and the mean height of the boys is 60 inches. One of the boys is 72 inches tall. Is the mean height of the other five boys greater than the mean height of the six girls? Explain.

9.3 Measures of Center
For use with Exploration 9.3

Learning Target: Find and interpret the median and mode of a data set.

Success Criteria:
- I can explain how the median and mode summarize a data set with a single number.
- I can find the median and mode of a data set.
- I can explain how changes to a data set affect the measures of center.
- I can use a measure of center to answer a statistical question.

---

1 EXPLORATION: Finding the Median

Work with a partner.

a. Write the total numbers of letters in the first and last names of 15 celebrities, historical figures, or people you know. One person is already listed for you.

Person	Number of Letters in First and Last Name
Abraham Lincoln	14

b. Order the values in your data set from least to greatest. Then write the data on a strip of grid paper with 15 boxes.

c. The *middle value* of the data set is called the *median*. The value (or values) that occur most often is called the *mode*. Find the median and the mode of your data set. Explain how you found your answers.

d. Why are the median and the mode considered averages of a data set?

9.3 Notetaking with Vocabulary

Vocabulary:

Notes:

9.3 Self-Assessment

Use the scale below to rate your understanding of the learning target and the success criteria.

1	2	3	4
I do not understand.	I can do it with help.	I can do it on my own.	I can teach someone else.

	Rating	Date
9.3 Measures of Center		
Learning Target: Find and interpret the median and mode of a data set.	1 2 3 4	
I can explain how the median and mode summarize a data set with a single number.	1 2 3 4	
I can find the median and mode of a data set.	1 2 3 4	
I can explain how changes to a data set affect the measures of center.	1 2 3 4	
I can use a measure of center to answer a statistical question.	1 2 3 4	

Big Ideas Math: Modeling Real Life Grade 6 **229**
Student Journal

9.3 Practice

Find the mean, median, and mode(s) of the data. Choose the measure that best represents the data. Explain your reasoning.

1. 83, 68, 56, 100, 78, 94, 74

2. 55, 65, 49, 22, 56, 65, 61, 57

3. 104, 128, 72, 73, 75, 73, 119

4. 20.1, 13.4, 9.8, 21.3, 20.8, 19.1, 68.1, 22.6

Find the mean, median, and mode(s) of the data with and without the outlier. Describe the effect of the outlier on the measures of central tendency.

5. 72, 75, 26, 65, 72, 67, 71

6. 70, 85, 150, 70, 85, 65, 65, 85

Find the mode(s) of the data.

7. A, B, D, C, D, B, A, B, C, B, A

8. X, Y, X, X, Y, Y, Y, X, X, Y, X, Y, X

9. A punter's first four punts in a football game are shown. After a fifth punt, the punter's mean was 30 yards. How long was the fifth punt? Explain how you found your answer.

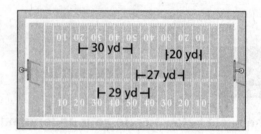

10. Each of five children picks out a birthday present for their mother. They share the total cost of the gifts equally.

Gift prices
$9.95
$10.25
$9.80
$9.95
$24.95

   a. Find the mean, median, and mode of the data.

   b. Which measure of center best represents the typical price of a gift? Explain.

   c. Which measure of center best represents each child's share of the cost? Explain.

   d. Each child received $3 from their grandfather to apply towards the gifts. Find the mean, median, and mode of the data with the $3 received by each child. How does this affect the mean, median, and mode of the data?

9.4 Measures of Variation
For use with Exploration 9.4

Learning Target: Find and interpret the range and interquartile range of a data set.

Success Criteria:
- I can explain how the range and interquartile range describe the variability of a data set with a single number.
- I can find the range and interquartile range of a data set.
- I can use the interquartile range to identify outliers.

1 EXPLORATION: Interpreting Statements

Work with a partner. There are 24 students in your class. Your teacher makes the following statements.

- **"The exam scores range from 75% to 96%."**

- **"Most of the students received high scores."**

a. What does each statement mean? Explain.

b. Use your teacher's statements to make a dot plot that can represent the distribution of the exam scores of the class.

c. Compare your dot plot with other groups'. How are they alike? different?

9.4 **Measures of Variation** (continued)

2 **EXPLORATION:** Grouping Data

Work with a partner. The numbers of U.S. states visited by students in a sixth-grade class are shown.

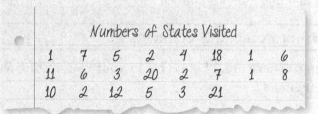

Numbers of States Visited

1	7	5	2	4	18	1	6
11	6	3	20	2	7	1	8
10	2	12	5	3	21		

a. Represent the data using a dot plot. Between what values do the data range?

b. Use the dot plot to make observations about the data.

c. How can you describe the *middle half* of the data?

9.4 Notetaking with Vocabulary

Vocabulary:

Notes:

9.4 Self-Assessment

Use the scale below to rate your understanding of the learning target and the success criteria.

1	2	3	4
I do not understand.	I can do it with help.	I can do it on my own.	I can teach someone else.

	Rating	Date
9.4 Measures of Variation		
Learning Target: Find and interpret the range and interquartile range of a data set.	1 2 3 4	
I can explain how the range and interquartile range describe the variability of a data set with a single number.	1 2 3 4	
I can find the range and interquartile range of a data set.	1 2 3 4	
I can use the interquartile range to identify outliers.	1 2 3 4	

9.4 Practice

Find the median, first quartile, third quartile, and interquartile range of the data.

1. 32, 53, 72, 66, 47, 54, 49, 67, 71

2. 142, 126, 145, 156, 132, 154, 149, 160, 153

3. 203, 183, 212, 181, 157, 204, 189, 190

4. 1.6, 3.7, 2.7, 9.1, 4.8, 5.7, 2.6, 8.6, 1.3, 9.9

5. Use the interquartile range to identify any outliers in Exercises 1–4.

6. The table shows the water level at the dock over a 12-hour period.

   a. Find and interpret the range of the water levels.

   b. Find and interpret the interquartile range of the water levels.

Water Level (feet)			
$3\frac{1}{4}$	$3\frac{3}{4}$	4	$4\frac{3}{4}$
$4\frac{1}{2}$	$4\frac{1}{4}$	$3\frac{1}{2}$	$3\frac{1}{4}$
3	$2\frac{3}{4}$	$2\frac{1}{4}$	2

7. The table shows the points earned by the contestants in a competition.

   a. Find and interpret the range of the points earned.

   b. Find and interpret the interquartile range of the points earned.

Points Earned			
15	12	17	8
21	20	6	9

   c. The second table shows the points earned by the contestants after 5 bonus points were awarded to each contestant. Find the range and interquartile range of the points earned after the bonus.

Points Earned After Bonus			
20	17	22	13
26	25	11	14

   d. If b more bonus points were added to each contestant, what would be the range and interquartile range of the points earned after the new bonus? Explain.

8. Create a set of data with 6 values that has a mode of 5, a median of 9, a range of 22, and an interquartile range of 10.

9. How does an outlier affect the interquartile range of a data set? Explain.

9.5 Mean Absolute Deviation
For use with Exploration 9.5

Learning Target: Find and interpret the mean absolute deviation of a data set.

Success Criteria:
- I can explain how the mean absolute deviation describes the variability of a data set with a single number.
- I can find the mean absolute deviation of a data set.
- I can compare data sets using the mean absolute deviation to draw conclusions.

1 EXPLORATION: Finding Distances from the Mean

Work with a partner. The table show the exam scores of 14 students in your class.

Exam Scores					
Ben	89	Omar	95	Dan	94
Emma	86	Hong	96	Lucy	89
Jeremy	80	Rob	92	Priya	84
Pete	80	Amy	90	Heather	85
Malik	96	Sue	76		

a. Which exam score deviates the most from the mean? Which exam score deviates the least from the mean? Explain how you found your answers.

b. How far is each data value from the mean?

c. Divide the sum of the values in part (b) by the number of values. In your own words, what does this represent?

d. In a data set, what does it mean when the value you found in part (c) is close to 0? Explain.

9.5 **Notetaking with Vocabulary**

Vocabulary:

Notes:

9.5 **Self-Assessment**

Use the scale below to rate your understanding of the learning target and the success criteria.

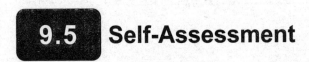

	Rating	Date
9.5 Mean Absolute Deviation		
Learning Target: Find and interpret the mean absolute deviation of a data set.	1 2 3 4	
I can explain how the mean absolute deviation describes the variability of a data set with a single number.	1 2 3 4	
I can find the mean absolute deviation of a data set.	1 2 3 4	
I can compare data sets using the mean absolute deviation to draw conclusions.	1 2 3 4	

Name_____ Date _____

9.5 Practice

Find the average distance of each data value in the set from the mean.

1. Numbers of marbles in a bag: 25, 42, 61, 33, 45, 50, 34, 42

2. Square footages of homes: 2052, 1250, 2200, 1856, 1442

Find and interpret the mean absolute deviation of the data. Round your answer to the nearest tenth, if necessary.

3.

Numbers of Squares in a Quilt			
8	20	16	12
24	18	32	30

4.

Numbers of Desks in a Classroom			
25	25	25	25
25	25	25	25

5.

Heights of Bleachers (feet)			
110	105.4	97.8	100
98.6	112.5	104.6	99.1

6.

Weights of Wrestlers (pounds)			
131.4	130.7	131.2	131.8
130.6	131.9	130.1	129.5

7. The data shows the prices of five shirts and five pairs of pants.

   Shirts: $15, $21, $18, $19, $24

   Pants: $25, $32, $40, $36, $29

   Find the MAD of each data set. Then compare their variations.

8. Add or subtract the MAD from the mean in the data set in Exercise 5.

   a. What percent of the values are within one MAD of the mean?

   b. What percent of the values are within two MADs of the mean?

   c. Which values are more than twice the MAD from the mean?

   d. Find the range and interquartile range for the data set. Use these values to give a possible explanation for the answer to part (b).

Name_____ Date_____

Chapter Self-Assessment

Use the scale below to rate your understanding of the learning target and
the success criteria.

1	2	3	4
I do not understand.	I can do it with help.	I can do it on my own.	I can teach someone else.

	Rating	Date
9.1 Introduction to Statistics		
Learning Target: Identify statistical questions and use data to answer statistical questions.	1 2 3 4	
I can recognize questions that anticipate a variety of answers.	1 2 3 4	
I can construct and interpret a dot plot.	1 2 3 4	
I can use data to answer a statistical question.	1 2 3 4	
9.2 Mean		
Learning Target: Find and interpret the mean of a data set.	1 2 3 4	
I can explain how the mean summarizes a data set with a single number.	1 2 3 4	
I can find the mean of a data set.	1 2 3 4	
I can use the mean of a data set to answer a statistical question.	1 2 3 4	
9.3 Measures of Center		
Learning Target: Find and interpret the median and mode of a data set.	1 2 3 4	
I can explain how the median and mode summarize a data set with a single number.	1 2 3 4	
I can find the median and mode of a data set.	1 2 3 4	
I can explain how changes to a data set affect the measures of center.	1 2 3 4	
I can use a measure of center to answer a statistical question.	1 2 3 4	

Name _____ Date _____

Chapter Self-Assessment (continued)

	Rating	Date
9.4 Measures of Variation		
Learning Target: Find and interpret the range and interquartile range of a data set.	1 2 3 4	
I can explain how the range and interquartile range describe the variability of a data set with a single number.	1 2 3 4	
I can find the range and interquartile range of a data set.	1 2 3 4	
I can use the interquartile range to identify outliers.	1 2 3 4	
9.5 Mean Absolute Deviation		
Learning Target: Find and interpret the mean absolute deviation of a data set.	1 2 3 4	
I can explain how the mean absolute deviation describes the variability of a data set with a single number.	1 2 3 4	
I can find the mean absolute deviation of a data set.	1 2 3 4	
I can compare data sets using the mean absolute deviation to draw conclusions.	1 2 3 4	

Name_____ Date_____

The bar graph shows the favorite types of salad dressings of the students in a class.

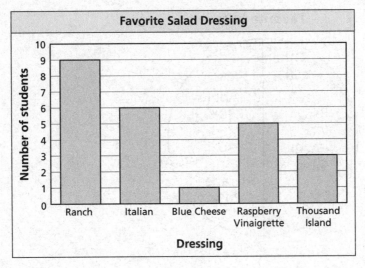

1. What salad dressing was chosen the most?

2. How many students said Raspberry Vinaigrette or Thousand Island is their favorite salad dressing?

3. How many students did *not* choose Italian as their favorite salad dressing?

4. How many students are in the class?

Review & Refresh (continued)

Chapter 10

The circle graph shows the results from a class survey on favorite juice. There are 30 students in the class.

Favorite Juice

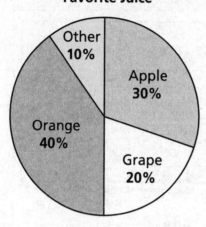

5. How many students said their favorite juice is apple?

6. How many students said their favorite juice is orange?

7. How many students said their favorite juice is grape?

Name_____ Date _____

Learning Target: Display and interpret data in stem-and-leaf plots.

Success Criteria:
- I can explain how to choose stems and leaves of a data set.
- I can make and interpret a stem-and-leaf plot.
- I can use a stem-and-leaf plot to describe the distribution of a data set.

---

1 EXPLORATION: Making a Data Display

Work with a partner. The list below gives the ages of women when they became first ladies of the United States.

 THE WHITE HOUSE
WASHINGTON, D.C.

Frances Cleveland - 21	Jacqueline Kennedy - 31
Caroline Harrison - 56	Claudia Johnson - 50
Ida McKinley - 49	Pat Nixon - 56
Edith Roosevelt - 40	Elizabeth Ford - 56
Helen Taft - 47	Rosalynn Carter - 49
Ellen Wilson - 52	Nancy Reagan - 59
Florence Harding - 60	Barbara Bush - 63
Grace Coolidge - 44	Hillary Clinton - 45
Lou Hoover - 54	Laura Bush - 54
Eleanor Roosevelt - 48	Michelle Obama - 45
Elizabeth Truman - 60	Melania Trump - 46
Mamie Eisenhower - 56	

a. The incomplete data display shows the ages of the first ladies in the left column of the list above. What do the numbers on the left represent? What do the numbers on the right represent?

Ages of First Ladies

2	1
3	
4	0 4 7 8 9
5	2 4 6 6
6	0 0

10.1 Stem-and-Leaf Plots (continued)

b. This data display is called a *stem-and-leaf plot*. What numbers do you think represent the *stems*? *leaves*? Explain your reasoning.

c. Complete the stem-and-leaf plot using the remaining ages.

d. Write a question about the ages of first ladies that is easier to answer using a stem-and-leaf plot than a dot plot.

10.1 Notetaking with Vocabulary

Vocabulary:

Notes:

10.1 Self-Assessment

Use the scale below to rate your understanding of the learning target and the success criteria.

1	2	3	4
I do not understand.	I can do it with help.	I can do it on my own.	I can teach someone else.

	Rating	Date
10.1 Stem-and-Leaf Plots		
Learning Target: Display and interpret data in stem-and-leaf plots.	1 2 3 4	
I can explain how to choose stems and leaves of a data set.	1 2 3 4	
I can make and interpret a stem-and-leaf plot.	1 2 3 4	
I can use a stem-and-leaf plot to describe the distribution of a data set.	1 2 3 4	

Name_____ Date _____

10.1 Practice

Make a stem-and-leaf plot of the data.

1.

Emails Sent			
55	12	37	42
35	56	9	16
38	31	12	45

2.

Burgers Sold			
36	60	72	18
8	75	60	54
42	36	20	36

The stem-and-leaf plot shows the weights (in pounds) of 15 pumpkins.

3. How many pumpkins weigh more than 10 pounds?

4. Find the mean, median, mode, range, and interquartile range of the data.

5. What percent of the pumpkins weigh more than the mean?

6. Describe the distribution of the data.

Stem	Leaf
0	6 8
1	2 6 8 8
2	0 1 3 6 9
3	2 4 8
4	
5	9

Key: 2|1 = 21 pounds

7. Which data value is the outlier? Describe how the outlier affects the mean.

8. What is significant about the row when the stem is 4?

9. The table shows the number of kittens adopted from a Humane Society each month for a year.

Number of Kittens Adopted			
January	12	July	19
February	21	August	22
March	23	September	21
April	31	October	24
May	25	November	31
June	18	December	42

a. Make a stem-and-leaf plot of the data.

b. During which month were the most kittens adopted? Make a conclusion about this.

c. What row in the stem-and-leaf plot had the most data items? What percent of the data items are in this row?

d. Find the mean and the mode of the data.

10.2 Histograms
For use with Exploration 10.2

Learning Target: Display and interpret data in histograms.

Success Criteria:
- I can explain how to draw a histogram.
- I can make and interpret a histogram.
- I can determine whether a question can be answered using a histogram.

1 EXPLORATION: Performing an Experiment

Work with a partner.

a. Make the airplane shown from a single sheet of $8\frac{1}{2}$-by-11-inch paper. Then design and make your own paper airplane.

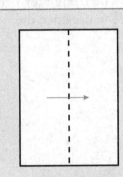

1. Fold in half. Then unfold.

2. Fold corners.

3. Fold corners again.

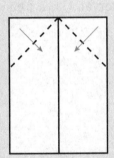

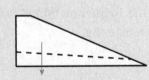

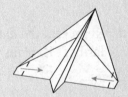

4. Fold in half.

5. Fold wings out on both sides.

6. Fold wing edges up.

10.2 Histograms (continued)

b. Fly each airplane 20 times. Keep track of the distance flown each time.

c. A **frequency table** groups data values into intervals. The **frequency** is the number of values in an interval. Use a frequency table to organize the results for each airplane.

d. Represent the data in the frequency tables graphically. Which airplane flies farther? Explain your reasoning.

10.2 Notetaking with Vocabulary

Vocabulary:

Notes:

10.2 Self-Assessment

Use the scale below to rate your understanding of the learning target and the success criteria.

1	2	3	4
I do not understand.	I can do it with help.	I can do it on my own.	I can teach someone else.

	Rating	Date
10.2 Histograms		
Learning Target: Display and interpret data in histograms.	1 2 3 4	
I can explain how to draw a histogram.	1 2 3 4	
I can make and interpret a histogram.	1 2 3 4	
I can determine whether a question can be answered using a histogram.	1 2 3 4	

10.2 Practice

Display the data in a histogram.

1.

Pages Typed	
Pages	**Frequency**
1–10	14
11–20	16
21–30	0
31–40	5

2.

Cookies Baked	
Cookies	**Frequency**
1–24	3
25–48	15
49–72	18
73–96	35

3. The histogram shows the number of waves caught by surfers at a beach one day.

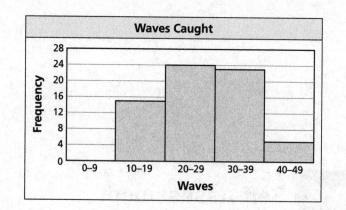

   a. Which interval contains the fewest data values?

   b. How many surfers were at the beach?

   c. What interval contains about 22% of the surfers?

   d. According to the histogram, is it possible that a surfer did not catch any waves that day? Explain.

   e. Would you conclude that this was a *good* or *bad* surfing day? Explain.

4. The table shows the cholesterol levels of 30 adults.

Cholesterol Levels					
180	195	225	220	182	165
199	260	304	187	285	325
300	250	185	220	157	289
310	246	214	180	301	295
205	200	189	260	305	303

   a. Make a histogram of the data starting with the interval 150-199.

   b. Make a histogram of the data starting with the interval 150-189.

   c. Which histogram has an approximately flat distribution, where the bars are about the same height?

   d. Which histogram allows you to better state how many adults have a cholesterol level below 300? Explain.

   e. Which histogram allows you to better state how many adults have a cholesterol level below 220? Explain.

Name_____ Date_____

10.3 Shapes of Distributions
For use with Exploration 10.3

Learning Target: Describe and compare shapes of distributions.

Success Criteria:
- I can explain what it means for a distribution to be skewed left, skewed right, or symmetric.
- I can use data displays to describe shapes of distributions.
- I can use shapes of distributions to compare data sets.

---

1 EXPLORATION: Describing Shapes of Distributions

Work with a partner. The lists show the first three digits and last four digits of several phone numbers in the contact list of a cell phone.

a. Compare and contrast the distribution of the last digit of each phone number to the distribution of the first digit of each phone number. Describe the shapes of the distributions.

538-	664-	-7253	-8678
438-	664-	-7290	-2063
664-	538-	-7200	-2911
761-	855-	-1192	-2103
868-	664-	-1142	-4328
735-	538-	-3500	-7826
694-	654-	-2531	-7957
599-	654-	-2079	-7246
725-	725-	-5897	-2119
556-	538-	-5341	-7845
555-	799-	-1392	-1109
456-	764-	-5406	-9154
736-	664-	-7875	-9018
664-	664-	-7335	-2184
576-	725-	-0494	-2367

Name _____ Date _____

10.3 **Shapes of Distributions** (continued)

b. Describe the shape of the distribution of the data in the table below.
Compare it to the distributions in part (a).

Ages of Cell Phones (years)					
0	1	0	6	4	0
2	3	5	1	1	2
0	1	2	3	1	0
0	0	1	1	1	1
7	1	4	2	2	2

10.3 Notetaking with Vocabulary

Vocabulary:

Notes:

10.3 Self-Assessment

Use the scale below to rate your understanding of the learning target and the success criteria.

1	2	3	4
I do not understand.	I can do it with help.	I can do it on my own.	I can teach someone else.

	Rating	Date
10.3 Shapes of Distributions		
Learning Target: Describe and compare shapes of distributions.	1 2 3 4	
I can explain what it means for a distribution to be skewed left, skewed right, or symmetric.	1 2 3 4	
I can use data displays to describe shapes of distributions.	1 2 3 4	
I can use shapes of distributions to compare data sets.	1 2 3 4	

Name _____ Date _____

10.3 Practice

Describe the shape of each distribution. Explain.

1.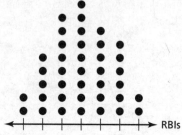

   Runs Batted In

2.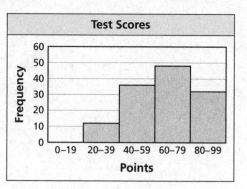

3. The frequency table shows the numbers of books read this month for the students in your class and the students in your friend's class.

Number of Books Read This Month	0	1	2	3	4	5
Your Class	0	3	6	8	7	6
Your Friend's Class	6	10	7	5	1	1

   a. Display the data for each class in a dot plot. Describe the shape of each distribution.

   b. Which class read more books? Explain.

   c. Which class has a greater mean? Explain.

   d. Which class has a lesser mode? Explain.

4. The table shows the number of videos rented each day.

   a. Make a histogram of the data starting with the interval 10–19. Describe the shape of the distribution.

   b. During the following week, the number of video rentals were: 25, 37, 38, 31, 22, 35, 24. Make a new histogram including the new video rental data.

   c. Describe the shape of the new distribution.

Videos Rented								
54	61	43	48	14	21	51	42	35
36	52	29	17	65	43	59	24	48
42	62	36	29	19	58	51	47	42

Name_____ Date_____

10.4 Choosing Appropriate Measures
For use with Exploration 10.4

Learning Target: Determine which measures of center and variation best describe a data set.

Success Criteria:
- I can describe the shape of a distribution.
- I can use the shape of a distribution to determine which measure of center best describes the data.
- I can use the shape of a distribution to determine which measure of variation best describes the data.

1 EXPLORATION: Using Shapes of Distributions

Work with a partner.

a. In Section 10.3 Exploration 1(a), you described the distribution of the first digits of the numbers at the right. In Exploration 1(b), you described the distribution of the data set below.

538-	664-
438-	664-
664-	538-
761-	855-
868-	664-
735-	538-
694-	654-
599-	654-
725-	725-
556-	538-
555-	799-
456-	764-
736-	664-
664-	664-
576-	725-

Ages of Cell Phones (years)					
0	1	0	6	4	0
2	3	5	1	1	2
0	1	2	3	1	0
0	0	1	1	1	1
7	1	4	2	2	2

What do you notice about the measures of center, measures of variation, and the shapes of the distributions? Explain.

10.4 **Choosing Appropriate Measures** (continued)

b. Which measure of center best describes each data set? Explain your reasoning.

c. Which measure of variation best describes each data set? Explain your reasoning.

Name_____ Date_____

 10.4 **Notetaking with Vocabulary**

Vocabulary:

Notes:

10.4 **Self-Assessment**

Use the scale below to rate your understanding of the learning target and the success criteria.

1	**2**	**3**	**4**
I do not understand.	I can do it with help.	I can do it on my own.	I can teach someone else.

	Rating	Date
10.4 Choosing Appropriate Measures		
Learning Target: Determine which measures of center and variation best describe a data set	1 2 3 4	
I can describe the shape of a distribution.	1 2 3 4	
I can use the shape of a distribution to determine which measure of center best describes the data.	1 2 3 4	
I can use the shape of a distribution to determine which measure of variation best describes the data.	1 2 3 4	

Name _____ Date _____

Choose the most appropriate measures to describe the center and the variation. Find the measures you choose.

1. Daily Running Distances

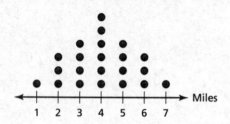

2. Number of Touchdowns

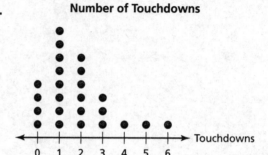

3. The frequency table shows the completion times of several chefs in a Bake-Off contest.

Completion Times (minutes)	20–24	25–29	30–34	35–39	40–44	45–49
Frequency	3	6	8	8	6	3

   a. Display the data in a histogram.

   b. What are the most appropriate measures to describe the center and variation? Explain.

   c. Can you find the exact values of the most appropriate measures that you chose? Explain.

4. Construct a dot plot for which the interquartile range is the most appropriate measure to describe the variation of the distribution.

5. You are measuring monthly home sales prices. Would you use the mean to describe the center and the MAD to describe the variation or the median to describe the center and the IQR to describe the variation? Explain your reasoning.

10.5 Box-and-Whisker Plots
For use with Exploration 10.5

Learning Target: Display and interpret data in box-and-whisker plots.

Success Criteria: • I can find the five-number summary of a data set.

• I can make a box-and-whisker plot.

• I can explain what the box and the whiskers of a box-and-whisker plot represent.

• I can compare data sets represented by box-and-whisker plots.

---

1   EXPLORATION: Drawing a Box-and-Whisker Plot

Work with a partner. Each student in a sixth-grade class is asked to choose a number from 1 to 20. The results are shown below.

Numbers Chosen			
4	5	14	16
5	16	17	8
18	13	17	18
17	14	19	11
15	8	2	18
13	19	8	7

a. The *box-and-whisker plot* below represents the data set. Which part represents the *box*? the *whiskers*? Explain.

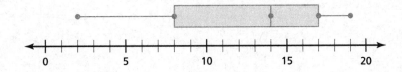

10.5 Box-and-Whisker Plots (continued)

b. What does each of the five plotted points represent?

c. In your own words, describe what a box-and-whisker plot is and what it tells you about a data set.

d. Conduct a survey in your class. Have each student write a number from 1 to 20 on a piece of paper. Collect all of the data and draw a box-and-whisker plot that represents the data. Compare the data with the box-and-whisker plot in part (a).

10.5 Notetaking with Vocabulary

Vocabulary:

Notes:

10.5 Self-Assessment

Use the scale below to rate your understanding of the learning target and the success criteria.

1	2	3	4
I do not understand.	I can do it with help.	I can do it on my own.	I can teach someone else.

	Rating	Date
10.5 Box-and-Whisker Plots		
Learning Target: Display and interpret data in box-and-whisker plots.	1 2 3 4	
I can find the five-number summary of a data set.	1 2 3 4	
I can make a box-and-whisker plot.	1 2 3 4	
I can explain what the box and the whiskers of a box-and-whisker plot represent.	1 2 3 4	
I can compare data sets represented by box-and-whisker plots.	1 2 3 4	

Name_____ Date _____

10.5 Practice

Make a box-and-whisker plot for the data.

1. Ages of buildings (in years): 12, 54, 30, 31, 48, 15, 20, 32, 1, 10, 13, 24

2. Selling prices of houses (in thousands of dollars): 40, 100, 82, 150, 124, 75, 54, 128, 112, 98, 76

3. The box-and-whisker plot represents the numbers of cars in airport parking lots.

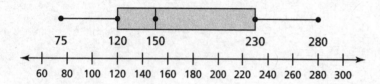

   a. What percent of the airport parking lots contain at least 230 cars?

   b. Is there more variability in the numbers of cars below 120 or above 230?

   c. Find and interpret the range of the data.

   d. What are the most appropriate measures to describe the center and variation of the distribution?

Identify the shape of the distribution. Explain.

4.   5.

6. A double box-and-whisker plot represents the stock prices of Company A and Company B over a 30-day period. Both companies have a minimum stock price of $3 and a maximum stock price of $10. The median stock price for Company A is $6 and the median stock price for Company B is $9.

   a. Which company is more likely to have a symmetric box-and-whisker plot? Explain.

   b. Which company has a more consistent stock price over the 30-day period?

Name_____ Date_____

 Chapter Self-Assessment

Use the scale below to rate your understanding of the learning target and
the success criteria.

1 I do not understand. **2** I can do it with help. **3** I can do it on my own. **4** I can teach someone else.

	Rating	Date
10.1 Stem-and-Leaf Plots		
Learning Target: Display and interpret data in stem-and-leaf plots.	1 2 3 4	
I can explain how to choose stems and leaves of a data set.	1 2 3 4	
I can make and interpret a stem-and-leaf plot.	1 2 3 4	
I can use a stem-and-leaf plot to describe the distribution of a data set.	1 2 3 4	
10.2 Histograms		
Learning Target: Display and interpret data in histograms.	1 2 3 4	
I can explain how to draw a histogram.	1 2 3 4	
I can make and interpret a histogram.	1 2 3 4	
I can determine whether a question can be answered using a histogram.	1 2 3 4	
10.3 Shapes of Distributions		
Learning Target: Describe and compare shapes of distributions.	1 2 3 4	
I can explain what it means for a distribution to be skewed left, skewed right, or symmetric.	1 2 3 4	
I can use data displays to describe shapes of distributions.	1 2 3 4	
I can use shapes of distributions to compare data sets.	1 2 3 4	

Chapter 10 Chapter Self-Assessment (continued)

	Rating	Date
10.4 Choosing Appropriate Measures		
Learning Target: Determine which measures of center and variation best describe a data set.	1 2 3 4	
I can describe the shape of a distribution.	1 2 3 4	
I can use the shape of a distribution to determine which measure of center best describes the data.	1 2 3 4	
I can use the shape of a distribution to determine which measure of variation best describes the data.	1 2 3 4	
10.5 Box-and-Whisker Plots		
Learning Target: Display and interpret data in box-and-whisker plots.	1 2 3 4	
I can find the five-number summary of a data set.	1 2 3 4	
I can make a box-and-whisker plot.	1 2 3 4	
I can explain what the box and the whiskers of a box-and-whisker plot represent.	1 2 3 4	
I can compare data sets represented by box-and-whisker plots.	1 2 3 4	

Photo Credits

75 irmetov/DigitalVision Vectors/Getty Images;
187 NASA; 200 ©iStockphoto.com/ingmar wesemann

Cover Image briddy_/iStock/Getty Images Plus

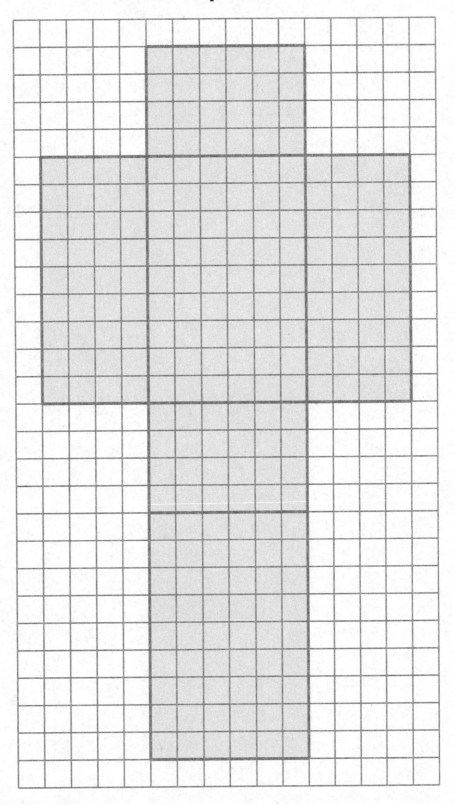

*Available at *BigIdeasMath.com.*

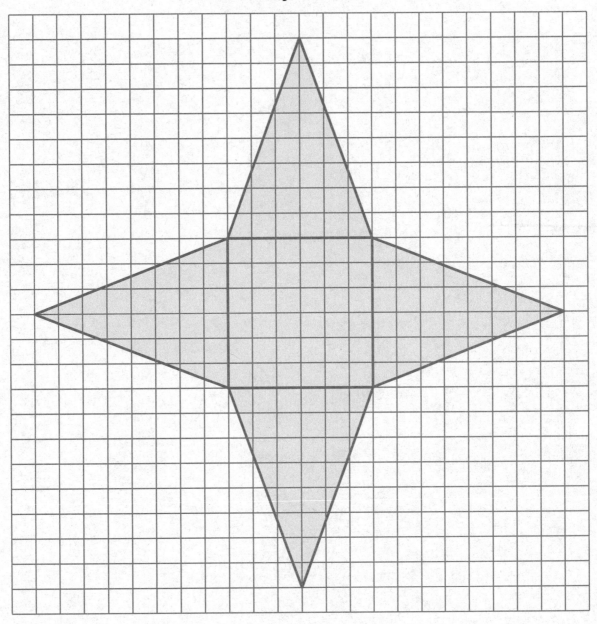